THE
PUZZLE
MURDERS

igloobooks

Contents

Detective Sergeant Katie McCrawley has a hunch.

She's convinced that the recent spate of murders in the small town of Graven End were all committed by one person: the notorious Puzzle Piece Killer, a serial killer who taunts the police by leaving unsolvable puzzles at the scene of each murder.

The problem is, no one else in the Homicide Division agrees with her theory, especially not her long-suffering boss, Detective Chief Inspector Charlie Turner, who has ordered her to drop it and: "get on with some actual police work, McCrawley, instead of wasting my time and patience".

Still, McCrawley is convinced, and decides to secretly pull all the evidence, revisit each of the six crime scenes and put together the clues in order to catch the serial killer that she *knows* is hiding somewhere in Graven End.

However, she can't do it alone. She needs you to help her work through the puzzles one by one and work out who has been committing these vile murders. Then, she can finally make an arrest and prove Inspector Turner wrong.

You will need considerable crime-solving knowledge and extensive puzzle-solving skills to tackle the case. Nothing you read from here on should be discounted. Everything you find in the following files is a clue and everyone should be considered a suspect until you prove them otherwise.

Everything you need to crack the case can be found in the following six files. There is a space on pages 232-233 to record any notes you feel are needed about the case.

So, are you in?

Meet the Team

Detective Sergeant Katie McCrawley

McCrawley has worked for the Police for 12 years, since leaving university. She started in community policing but quickly rose through the ranks after her superiors noticed her ability to put clues together quickly. She became the youngest female detective in the force. She can be a bit abrasive, and will often irritate her colleagues without realising.

Detective Chief Inspector Charlie Turner

DCI Turner has very little time for time-wasters. He is a no-nonsense boss, who terrifies new members of the team with his loud voice and big stature. He is, however, secretly rather fond of his team, sincerely believing them to be the best of the best. Before he joined the police force, he worked in the Graven End Crime Laboratory.

Coroner Doctor Alan Easton

As the local coroner for Graven End, Dr. Easton has attended each of the six crime scenes. The Crime Scene Technicians spend their time finding ways to work around his forgetfulness. He is an amateur magician, entertaining the officers at crime scenes instead of working. At university he specialised in methods used to determine the time of death.

Detective Constable Alex Summers

Summers is accidentally good at his job, often stumbling across clues and unintentionally solving crimes that would take others a lot of hard work and overtime. It's given him the reputation in the department as a whizz kid, a crime-solving savant. Really, he has absolutely no idea what is going on most of the time, and he is fine with that.

This is the team you'll be working with. Use everything they tell you to help solve the case and catch the killer.

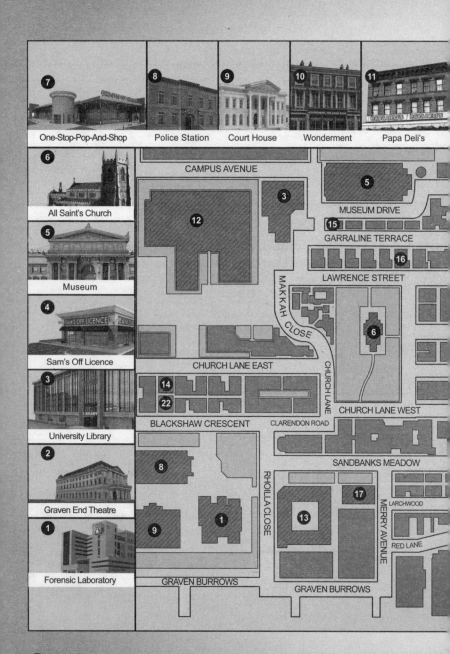

One-Stop-Pop-And-Shop · Police Station · Court House · Wonderment · Papa Deli's

All Saint's Church

Museum

Sam's Off Licence

University Library

Graven End Theatre

Forensic Laboratory

CAMPUS AVENUE

MUSEUM DRIVE

GARRALINE TERRACE

LAWRENCE STREET

MAKKAH CLOSE

CHURCH LANE

CHURCH LANE EAST

CHURCH LANE WEST

BLACKSHAW CRESCENT

CLARENDON ROAD

SANDBANKS MEADOW

RHOILLA CLOSE

MERRY AVENUE

LARCHWOOD

RED LANE

GRAVEN BURROWS

GRAVEN BURROWS

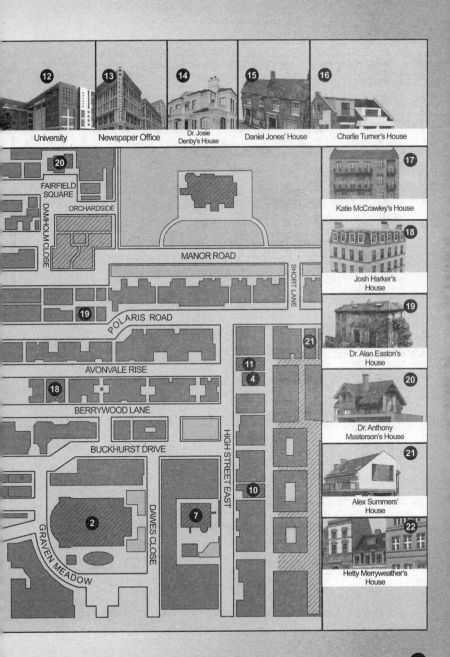

12 University

13 Newspaper Office

14 Dr. Josie Denby's House

15 Daniel Jones' House

16 Charlie Turner's House

17 Katie McCrawley's House

18 Josh Harker's House

19 Dr. Alan Easton's House

20 Dr. Anthony Masterson's House

21 Alex Summers' House

22 Hetty Merryweather's House

20

FAIRFIELD SQUARE

ORCHARDSIDE

DAMHOLM CLOSE

MANOR ROAD

SHORT LANE

19

POLARIS ROAD

AVONVALE RISE

18

BERRYWOOD LANE

11

4

21

BUCKHURST DRIVE

HIGH STREET EAST

DAWES CLOSE

10

2

7

GRAVEN MEADOW

How to Solve the Puzzles

The killer has an extensive knowledge of puzzle types. One of the officers has compiled a "how-to", for internal reference. Some will be familiar to you while others might not be.

A-Z
Each letter of the alphabet has been removed from the grid once, to leave 26 empty squares. Work out which letter fits in each of the blank squares.

ARROW WORDS
Answer the clues in the grid in the direction of each arrow.

BATTLESHIPS
Locate the position of each of the "ships" listed in the grid. Numbers around the edge show the number of segments in each row and column of the puzzle. "Ships" are surrounded on all sides by water, including diagonally.

JOURNEYS
Deduce a journey, visiting each square once, starting at 1 and ending at 100. Move one square in any direction at a time, including diagonally.

JIGSAW SUDOKU
Place the numbers 1-9 once in each row, column and bold-lined jigsaw region composed of nine cells.

KRISS KROSS
Each word must be placed in the grid once to solve the puzzle. Work out where each word goes in order to complete the grid.

PATHFINDER
Moving from letter to adjacent letter, find a path that visits every square and spells out words associated with the given theme. Start on the shaded square.

SUDOKU / LETTER-DOKU
Place each number from 1-9 once into each of the rows, columns and boxes in the grid. In Letter-Doku, the letters A-I replace the numbers 1-9.

CODEBREAKER
Work out which letter of the alphabet is represented by each number from 1-26, and place that letter in the grid wherever the number occurs.

KAKURO
Fill the white squares so that the total in each across or down run of cells matches the total at the start of that run. Use the numbers from 1-9 only and do not repeat a number in a run.

Investigation opened into death of teenager found in alleyway

Less than 48 hours after the discovery of Josh Harker's body in the alleyway behind his workplace, Papa Deli's Pizzeria in Graven End, the police have declared the death suspicious and announced that an investigation into the death has begun. While the statement named the officer in charge of the investigation (Detective Sergeant Katie McCrawley), no further details were given about the circumstances surrounding the death of the nineteen-year-old university student.

The Harker family told *The New Graven End News* they welcomed the news of the police investigation into the death of Josh. They would cooperate fully in any way that they could, but ask that "they please be left alone to grieve their beloved Josh".

Friends, family and local residents have been laying flowers and messages of sorrow in front of the cordoned-off alley where Josh was found by Sam Dreyfuss, owner of the off-licence on the high street next to Papa Deli's, in the early hours of yesterday morning. One friend, who didn't want to be named, called Josh "the kindest, most lovely friend anyone could ask for".

Mass expulsion at Graven End University after plagiarism-for-profit discovered

Nine students were officially expelled today after a three-month long investigation by the Academic Integrity Department at Graven End University uncovered an elaborate plagiarism ring, where three third-year medical students were offering essays for cash. Their downfall came when one of the professors recognised a recently submitted essay as a copy of one that was submitted by another student less than two years ago.

This isn't the first time the medical department at Graven End University has been rocked by a plagiarism scandal. More than forty years ago, medical student Leo Santana was one of two students found to have plagiarised more than half of their assignments during their four year attendance. The discovery was made by Dr Anthony Masterson, then Head of the Medical Department, and Daniel Jones, leader of the Academic Integrity Department. The widely publicised scandal rocked the local community. Santana was named and publicly expelled, but the other student's name was never released, and privately was allowed to quit.

At a time when medical students were considered to be upstanding members of society, the disgrace and public embarrassment heaped upon Leo led to his entire family moving away from Graven End under a cloud.

The University released a statement this morning

CRIME SCENE ONE

<u>ONE</u>

LOCATION:
Inside a dumpster in the alley behind Papa Deli's Pizzeria, High Street.

MURDER WEAPON:
Metal dumpster

ELEMENTS OF THE FILE HAVE BEEN REDACTED DUE TO THE HIGHLY CONFIDENTIAL NATURE OF THE CASE. THE FILE AND CONTENTS ARE THE PROPERTY OF THE GRAVEN END POLICE DEPARTMENT. REMOVAL FROM THE BUILDING WILL RESULT IN IMMEDIATE ARREST.

VICTIM:
Josh Harker

Harker is found inside the dumpster out the back of the pizza place where he worked as a delivery boy. The killer must have managed to get the victim's attention. █████████████████████████

███████████████████████████████

It is suggested that Harker stuck his head out—potentially in reaction to a noise—and that's when the killer slammed the lid down on his neck, breaking it instantly.

Detectives find a number of pieces of paper around the dumpster, but dismiss them all as trash. Still, ████████████████████████████ takes them into evidence.

This pizza leaflet is found tucked into the victim's shirt pocket. Some of the letters have been blacked out. Can you work out the missing letters and find out if the killer left a message behind?

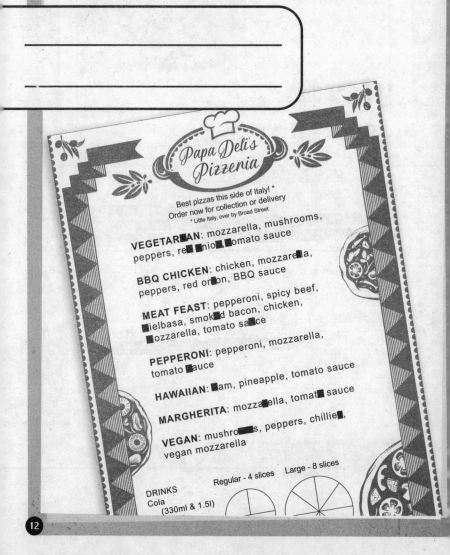

Papa Deli's Pizzeria

Best pizzas this side of Italy! *
Order now for collection or delivery
* Little Italy, over by Broad Street

VEGETAR■AN: mozzarella, mushrooms, peppers, re■ ■nio■, ■omato sauce

BBQ CHICKEN: chicken, mozzare■la, peppers, red on■on, BBQ sauce

MEAT FEAST: pepperoni, spicy beef, ■ielbasa, smok■d bacon, chicken, ■ozzarella, tomato sa■ce

PEPPERONI: pepperoni, mozzarella, tomato ■auce

HAWAIIAN: ■am, pineapple, tomato sauce

MARGHERITA: mozza■ella, tomat■ sauce

VEGAN: mushro■■s, peppers, chillie■, vegan mozzarella

Regular - 4 slices   Large - 8 slices

DRINKS
Cola
(330ml & 1.5l)

```
H  P  X  X  I  R  S  W  E  E  T  C  O  R  N
H  L  I  S  E  I  V  O  H  C  N  A  E  S  M
N  O  I  N  O  C  A  B  T  U  N  A  U  S  U
S  A  S  Q  E  J  J  A  L  A  P  E  N  O  S
O  S  K  E  G  A  S  U  A  S  I  W  N  L  H
K  G  S  R  E  P  P  E  P  E  C  E  B  I  R
S  Q  C  B  M  R  W  P  S  U  K  J  Z  V  O
P  R  S  I  R  I  B  L  L  C  I  U  X  E  O
H  A  A  I  U  E  T  C  I  E  H  L  L  S  M
I  S  L  M  C  R  H  H  T  B  E  E  F  N  Z
E  V  A  S  Z  O  C  O  K  R  O  T  E  T  E
S  H  M  N  W  E  S  R  F  A  R  A  I  S  O
A  H  I  C  A  S  D  I  E  B  I  T  S  P  E
R  S  Q  Y  S  Q  T  Z  L  U  P  T  A  S  E
B  C  Q  O  T  A  M  O  T  A  N  R  B  T  R
```

ANCHOVIES	HAM	PEPPERS
BACON	HERBS	PINEAPPLE
BARBECUE SAUCE	JALEPENOS	SALAMI
BEEF	MUSHROOM	SAUSAGE
CHEESE	OLIVES	SWEETCORN
CHICKEN	ONION	TOMATO
CHORIZO	PEPPERONI	TUNA

Dr. Easton finds this word search in the victim's shoe prior to the autopsy. One of the words from the list does not appear in the word search. Can you work out which one?

Sara's PUZZLE PAGES

THE BEST-SELLING NEWSPAPER IN GRAVEN END

Crossword

PUZZLE
3

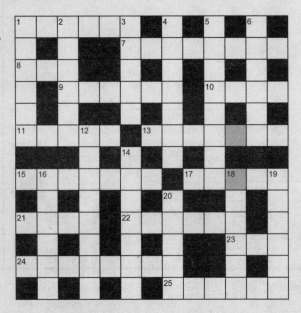

Across

1 Modern ballroom dance (3-3)
7 Speaks very quietly (8)
8 ___ Titmuss: TV personality (3)
9 Lure (6)
10 Chemical salt used in dyeing (4)
11 Long pointed elephant teeth (5)
13 Marked like a zebra (7)
15 Changed gradually over time (7)
17 Sum of money wagered (5)
21 Affirm solemnly (4)
22 Made fun of playfully (6)
23 ___ Tyler: actress (3)
24 Where one finds Glasgow (8)
25 E.g. summer (6)

Down

1 Item of neckwear (6)
2 Excuses of any kind (6)
3 Not asleep (5)
4 Composed or serious manner (7)
5 Beekeeper (8)
6 Game bird; grumble (6)
12 Unit of power (8)
14 In the middle (7)
16 In a lively manner (6)
18 Mixes up or confuses (6)
19 Ten plus one (6)
20 Attacks without warning (5)

> ## Remember, it's always the small pieces that make up the big picture!

A - Z

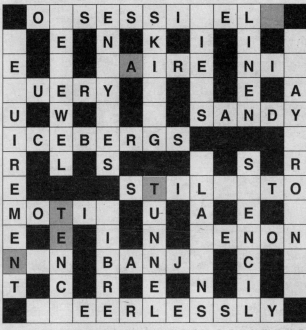

PUZZLE
4

A B C D E F G H I J K L M N O P Q R S T U V W X Y Z

After the victim's body is removed from the dumpster, McCrawley discovers a photo of the very same dumpster, left on top of the pile of trash underneath the body.

An additional photo is taken by the Crime Scene Techs. Can you determine **seven** differences between the two photographs?

PUZZLE
6

Kriss Kross

3 letters
Ash
Eel
Eve
Foe
Lye
Nee
Nib
Not
Rev
Tor

5 letters
Ensue
Night
Poems
Thorn

6 letters
Butane
Eyelid
Ornate
Phylum
Sprang
Warden

7 letters
Placebo
Ravages

8 letters
Eleventh
Munchies

9 letters
Alleviate
Effectual
Statistic
Synthetic

10 letters
Betterment
Crescendos
Fatherland
Submarines

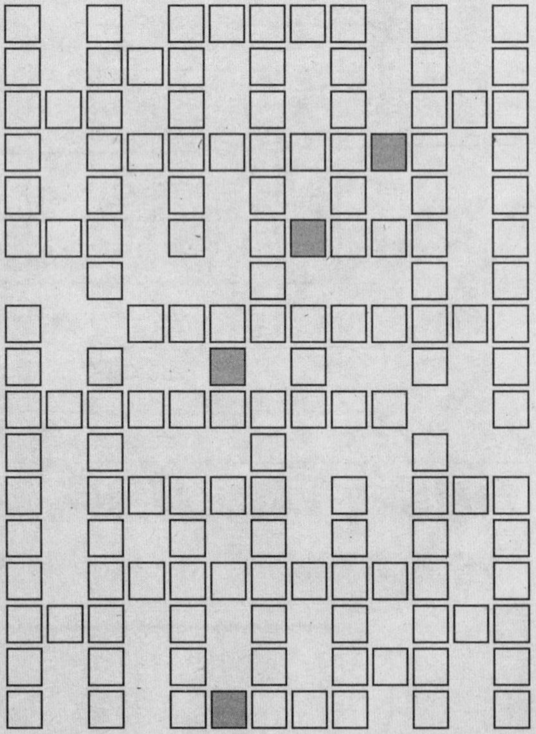

Jigsaw Sudoku

PUZZLE 7

	2							
	4				2		1	
	7							
	9		5			2		3
			3					
5			8	3	7			
2		1	4					
		8						
		4	2					

19

A scrap of paper is found in the victim's pocket.
It looks like the victim listed his delivery locations
in a type of shorthand. Can you use the Graven End map
on pages 6-7 and the Papa Deli's leaflet on page 12 to
determine which pizzas went where?

8.25 - Me - ShL
8.30 - Pep (+mush) - PR
8.40 - Me, Veg - AR
8.45 - BBQ x2 - GrM
8.50 - Veg x2, V, Marg, Me x2 - Rho

-

9.15 - Haw (+bacon), Marg, Me x2 - CLE
9.25 - Marg x2, BBQ x2 - Mak
9.35 - BBQ (no pep) - Or
9.40 - Me, Pep x2 - FSq
9.45 - Veg, Pep - FSq

-

10.05 - Pep x3, Veg x2, BBQ x4,
          V x2 - Cam
10.15 - Marg x 2, Pep, Haw (ex. pine) - MR
10.25 - Pep (+bacon, +mush), Pep - AR
10.30 - Pep, Me - Da

```
8.25  - Me - ShL                    . . . . . . . . . . . . . . . . . . . . . .
8.30  - Pep (+mush) - PR            . . . . . . . . . . . . . . . . . . . . . .
8.40  - Me, Veg - AR                . . . . . . . . . . . . . . . . . . . . . .
8.45  - BBQ x2 - GrM                . . . . . . . . . . . . . . . . . . . . . .
8.50  - Veg x2, V, Marg, Me
        x2 - Rho                    . . . . . . . . . . . . . . . . . . . . . .
9.15  - Haw (+bacon), Marg,
        Me x2 - CLE                 . . . . . . . . . . . . . . . . . . . . . .
9.25  - Marg x2, BBQ x2 - Mak       . . . . . . . . . . . . . . . . . . . . . .
9.35  - BBQ (no pep) - Or           . . . . . . . . . . . . . . . . . . . . . .
9.40  - Me, Pep x2 - FSq            . . . . . . . . . . . . . . . . . . . . . .
9.45  - Veg, Pep - FSq              . . . . . . . . . . . . . . . . . . . . . .
10.05 - Pep x3, Veg x2, BBQ
        x4, V x2 - Cam              . . . . . . . . . . . . . . . . . . . . . .
10.15 - Marg x 2, Pep, Haw
        (ex. pine)- MR              . . . . . . . . . . . . . . . . . . . . . .
10.25 - Pep (+bacon, +mush),
        Pep - AR                    . . . . . . . . . . . . . . . . . . . . . .
10.30 - Pep, Me - Da                . . . . . . . . . . . . . . . . . . . . . .
```

> The following pizzas are found beside the
> dumpster in the victim's delivery bag. Using the
> delivery route, can you work out a rough time
> frame for the murder? **3 Meat Feast, 1 Margherita,
> 3 Vegetarian, 2 BBQ Chicken, and 1 Vegan.**

_____ pm

Sara's PUZZLE PAGES

THE BEST-SELLING NEWSPAPER IN GRAVEN END

Crossword

PUZZLE
9

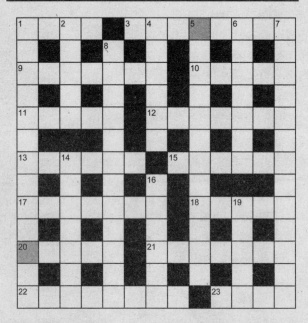

Across

1 Tall cereal grass (4)
3 Soft-bodied beetle (4-4)
9 A very long time ago (4,3)
10 Imposing poems (5)
11 Speed music is played at (5)
12 Concerned just with oneself (7)
13 Bad-tempered mythical creature (6)
15 Notable inconvenience (6)
17 One more (7)
18 Music with a recurrent theme (5)
20 Divide by two (5)
21 Freshness (7)
22 Act of moving around an axis (8)
23 Resist; refuse to obey (4)

Down

1 Codebreaker (13)
2 Furnish with new weapons (5)
4 Most recent (6)
5 Small garden carts (12)
6 Starting points (7)
7 Naughtily (13)
8 Firm rebuke (12)
14 Pamphlet (7)
16 Quickly (6)
19 Female relation (5)

Codebreaker

PUZZLE 10

19	1	9	13	14	8			16		12	26	12
	16		9		26	25	9	11	6		11
8	21	6	13	9	8	21		7		11		5
	11			11		21		21	5	11	18	8
15	5	11	21	8	1	9	14			6		3
	14			24		11		9		10		5
11	9	2	26	1	16		8	16	9	9	20	9
6		1		16		8		15			26	
1		16			15	4	26	1	11	12	26	19
16	1	10	4	21		26		11			13	
12		13		11		11	5	15	21	1	26	16
26		9	23	1	15	21		13			10	
17	6	8		22			20	9	25	4	19	11

A B C D E F G H I J K L M N O P Q R S T U V W X Y Z

1	2	3	4	5	6	7	8	9	10	11	12	13
I	J											

14	15	16	17	18	19	20	21	22	23	24	25	26
D												

Turn me on my side and I am everything. but cut me in half and I am nothing. What am I?

A bookcase is full of books. If on the top shelf a book is fourth from the left and sixth from the right. how many books are there on that shelf?

If 9 is 4 and 22 is 9. what is 18?

The victim's backpack is found next to the dumpster. A three-number combination lock has been slipped between the zippers of the main compartment, and the above piece of paper is found folded up in the front pocket. Can you work out the combination lock by answering the riddles?

After getting the lock off the backpack, Crime Scene Techs are disappointed to discover it is almost completely empty. It contains just one piece of paper, neatly folded, with the following crossword on it.

Across
1 Finely chopped (8)
5 Blue dye (4)
8 Friend (Spanish) (5)
9 Reconstruct (7)
10 Engraving (7)
12 The North Star (7)
14 Scottish national emblem (7)
16 Table support (7)
18 Responded to (7)
19 Alphabetical list in a book (5)
20 Foolish (4)
21 Dreariness (8)

Down
1 Total spread of a bridge (4)
2 Nasal (6)
3 Reduces perspiration (9)
4 Eagles' nests (6)
6 Establish by law (6)
7 Emissary (8)
11 Inquisitiveness (9)
12 Ambled (8)
13 On ___ of: in the interests of (6)
14 Showing gentleness (6)
15 Walk laboriously (6)
17 Hatchets (4)

PUZZLE
13

Sam Dreyfuss, owner of the off-licence next door to the pizza shop, comes forward and mentions that he had heard a repeated banging sound last night. "As if someone was banging on metal", he said. The team pulls his CCTV tapes, but the camera is pointing in the wrong direction and they can't get a glimpse of the killer. However, the banging sound can still be heard.

```
.. /
.-- .. .-.. .-.. /
-... . /
-... .- -.-. -.- /
...- . .-. -.-- /
... --- --- -. /
-... ..- - /
.. /
.-- --- -. - /
-... . /
- .... . /
... .- -- . /
.--. . .-. ... --- -. /
.- --. .- .. -.
```

A: .-	M: --	Y: -.--
B: -...	N: -.	Z: --..
C: -.-.	O: ---	0: -----
D: -..	P: .--.	1: .----
E: .	Q: --.-	2: ..---
F: ..-.	R: .-.	3: ...--
G: --.	S: ...	4: ....-
H:	T: -	5: .....
I: ..	U: ..-	6: -....
J: .---	V: ...-	7: --...
K: -.-	W: .--	8: ---..
L: .-..	X: -..-	9: ----.

One of the Crime Scene Techs points out that it sounds like Morse code. Can you work out the message the killer left behind for us to hear?

_ / _ _ _ _ / _ _ /

_ _ _ _ / _ _ _ _ /

_ _ _ _ /

_ _ _ / _ / _ _ _ _ /

_ _ / _ _ _ /

_ _ _ _/ _ _ _ _ _

Sara's PUZZLE PAGES

THE BEST-SELLING NEWSPAPER IN GRAVEN END

Word Search: Everything starts with a G

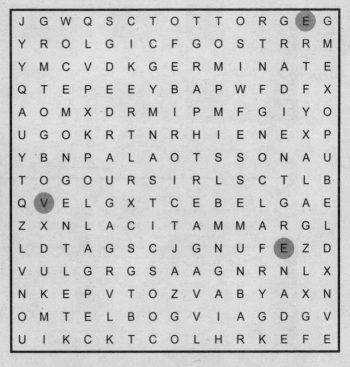

PUZZLE 14

J	G	W	Q	S	C	T	O	T	T	O	R	G	E	G
Y	R	O	L	G	I	C	F	G	O	S	T	R	R	M
Y	M	C	V	D	K	G	E	R	M	I	N	A	T	E
Q	T	E	P	E	E	Y	B	A	P	W	F	D	F	X
A	O	M	X	D	R	M	I	P	M	F	G	I	Y	O
U	G	O	K	R	T	N	R	H	I	E	N	E	X	P
Y	B	N	P	A	L	A	O	T	S	S	O	N	A	U
T	O	G	O	U	R	S	I	R	L	S	C	T	L	B
Q	V	E	L	G	X	T	C	E	B	E	L	G	A	E
Z	X	N	L	A	C	I	T	A	M	M	A	R	G	L
L	D	T	A	G	S	C	J	G	N	U	F	E	Z	D
V	U	L	G	R	G	S	A	A	G	N	R	N	L	X
N	K	E	P	V	T	O	Z	V	A	B	Y	A	X	N
O	M	T	E	L	B	O	G	V	I	A	G	D	G	V
U	I	K	C	K	T	C	O	L	H	R	K	E	F	E

GALAXY	GLORY	GRAMMATICAL
GALLOP	GNOME	GRAPH
GENTLE	GOBLET	GRENADE
GERBIL	GOGGLE	GROTTO
GERMINATE	GOVERNOR	GUARDED
GLASS	GRADIENT	GYMNASTICS
GLEBE	GRAFFITI	GYRFALCON

Arrow Words

PUZZLE 15

Railway vehicle	▼	Miserly	▼	Jar lids	▼	Unwell	Close at hand	Chatter
Sociable						▼	▼	▼
Ripped		Herb		Prayer ▶				
▶		▼		Stone block ▶				
Foolish people (informal) ▶					Liability	High spirits		People who rent property
▶				Detection technology ▶		▼		▼
Young kangaroo		Tends (anag)	Result	▼	Strong alkaline solution ▶			
Thought ▶		▼	▼		Volcano in Sicily		Solicit custom	
Feud ▶					▼		▼	
▶								
Feeling	Number of attendees ▶							
Exploit unfairly ▶			Social insects ▶					

29

Transcript of telephone conversation between Detective Sergeant Katie McCrawley and Detective Constable Alex Summers.

McCrawley: Hello?

Summers: Hey, it's me.

McCrawley: I guessed. What's up?

Summers: We didn't find anything else in the bag apart from the crossword.

McCrawley: What was the crossword pointing us to?

Summers: Oh, polaris. Not sure why they wanted us to pay attention to the North Star, but there you are.

McCrawley: Then assume it's not about the North Star. Do we know any other polaris?

Summers: None that I can remember. I'll look back.

McCrawley: Okay, and the bag was a dead end?

Summers: Yup. Not like these alleyways. I've already gotten lost about four times.

McCrawley: Have you organised a sweep of the alleys?

Summers: No?

McCrawley: You're a pain. Okay, do that and then call me. [ends call]

[END OF TRANSCRIPT]

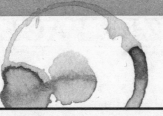

Summers has a map of the alleyways behind the pizza shop made, so that a thorough search can be started. Can you plot a route through the alleys out to the road?

Sara's PUZZLE PAGES

Kakuro

PUZZLE 17

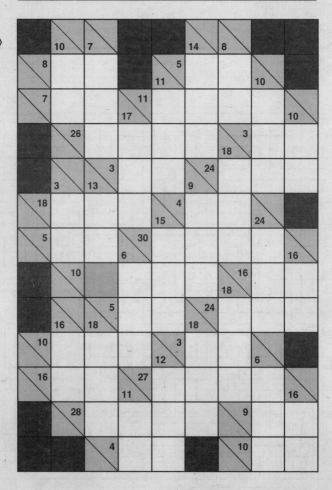

Pathfinder: Cities in Tennessee

PUZZLE
18

T	E	G	R	O	E	G	Y	D	N
O	U	R	N	K	N	B	G	S	A
W	B	G	A	L	I	I	I	B	R
N	S	F	R	P	M	R	C	V	E
L	R	E	I	H	E	M	H	I	R
A	V	Y	S	M	T	T	W	C	K
R	E	D	L	I	E	L	O	U	D
G	U	T	L	I	R	T	O	N	A
N	G	A	R	N	A	B	D	R	Y
E	F	A	R	G	T	O	N	S	M

BARTLETT	DYERSBURG	LA VERGNE
BIG SANDY	FARRAGUT	MEMPHIS
BIRCHWOOD	FRANKLIN	MILLINGTON
DUCK RIVER	GEORGETOWN	SMYRNA

We only regret the puzzles we didn't finish.

One of the officers involved in the alleyway search
finds a Journeys puzzle printed on tracing paper.
Summers notices that, when it is overlaid with the
map, it forms a perfect grid. Can you work out down
which alley the killer has left the next clue?

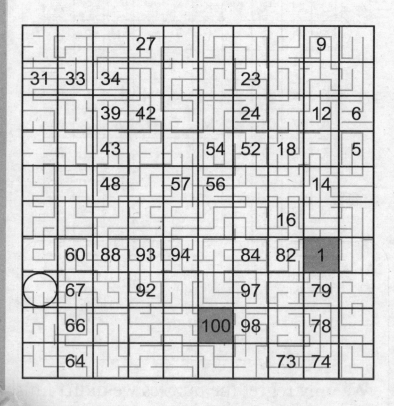

At the end of the alleyway is a door, with five numbered keys dangling from the frame and a piece of paper taped underneath. Can you use the clues to find the correct key?

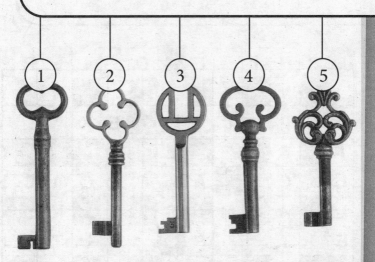

Using the clues, can you determine the order of the keys and which is the right key to open the door?
1: This key is somewhere to the left of the key to the door.
2: This key is not at one of the ends.
3: This key is three spaces away from the key to the door (2 between).
4: This key is next to the key to the door.
5: This key is directly in the middle.

One of these keys will open the door.

Sara's PUZZLE PAGES

THE BEST-SELLING NEWSPAPER IN GRAVEN END

A - Z

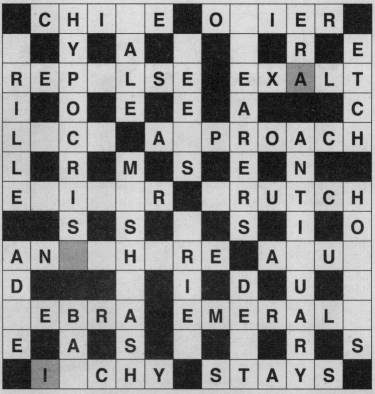

A B C D E F G H I J K L M N O P Q R S T U V W X Y Z

There's power in words and in puzzles.

Kriss Kross

3 letters
Chi
Elk
Gee
Hue
Pet
Sky
Use

4 letters
Beer
Isle
Knap
Nova
Ours
Putt
Rein
Rich
Taxi
Tows

5 letters
Camel
Enjoy

6 letters
Exotic
Yearns

7 letters
Chamber
Coxcomb
Degrees
Extinct
Offence
Padlock
Radiant
Retsina

8 letters
Athletic
Earnings
Kindling
Skeletal

9 letters
Judgement
Pseudonym

When the officers open the door a small combination safe is
found inside. A piece of paper slipped underneath the safe
has the words "Open with three but leave the four" written
on it. Summers tries pressing just the 3 button, but it
doesn't work. Can you work out how to open the safe?

1	2	3
4	5	6
7	8	9
10	11	12
13	14	15

GI	VK	EE	SF	AH
IL	DJ	NL	GO	HM
UE	SP	HK	RG	RO
OS	DM	SL	SV	OD
MF	KA	HN	YD	TF
KI	JM	EF	SS	IE
TD	KW	HA	SK	BH
ID	KS	OB	JW	FN
FG	AS	UK	JL	TN

Opening the safe reveals yet another piece of paper.
Try deleting one letter from each pair to discover
the killer's final message.

Sara's PUZZLE PAGES

THE BEST-SELLING NEWSPAPER IN GRAVEN END

Codebreaker

PUZZLE
25

10		10		13				9		25		10
13	14	12	26	15	12		3	25	7	11	12	4
23		13		10		21		25		5		13
3	13	4	14	12	21	23		11	12	12	20	21
12		6		4		13		25		4		19
4	25	25	20		8	4	25	10	21			
21		17		2		23		1		6		21
		22	15	13	11	24		16	12	26	23
21		19		26		18		14		26		15
20	3	13	20	18		26	12	13	4	12	21	23
18		21		19		10		16		8		23
24	25	23	11	12	1		11	15	19	18	26	12
19		1		4				13		23		4

A B C D E F G H I J K L M N O P Q R S T U V W X Y Z

1	2	3	4	5	6	7	8	9	10	11	12	13
						W						

14	15	16	17	18	19	20	21	22	23	24	25	26
V							S					

40

Word Search: Delicious Side Dishes

PUZZLE 26

BREAD
BROCCOLI
CARROT SOUP
CHEESE
CHIPS
COLESLAW
GREEN BEANS
MASHED POTATO
MIXED SALAD
NACHOS
NEW POTATOES
ONION TART
PATATAS BRAVAS
POTATO SALAD
POTATO SKINS
POTATO WEDGES
RICE
SARDINES
SCALLOPS
SMOKED SALMON
SUMMER SALAD

N	K	I	L	O	C	C	O	R	B	R	E	A	D	P
E	P	S	C	A	L	L	O	P	S	W	O	Z	S	Y
W	C	P	S	U	M	M	E	R	S	A	L	A	D	N
P	P	C	O	M	R	M	T	A	J	L	P	H	A	O
O	O	T	A	T	O	P	D	E	H	S	A	M	L	C
T	T	T	R	R	A	K	S	D	E	E	G	L	A	G
A	A	I	A	A	R	T	E	O	D	L	A	P	S	R
T	T	E	L	T	T	O	O	D	H	O	A	S	D	E
O	O	O	C	A	O	N	T	W	S	C	T	S	E	E
E	S	E	E	H	C	S	O	S	E	A	A	Q	X	N
S	K	C	T	Z	I	D	A	I	O	D	L	N	I	B
G	I	I	U	Y	U	P	S	L	N	U	G	M	M	E
I	N	R	B	K	L	U	S	I	A	O	P	E	O	A
S	S	A	R	D	I	N	E	S	T	D	E	R	S	N
S	A	V	A	R	B	S	A	T	A	T	A	P	H	S

Great puzzles take time.

41

Use this page to record any notes or answers
for this crime. This may help you to determine
who you think the killer is at the very end.

PUZZLE	ANSWER
1	
2	
5	
8	
11	
12	
13	
16	
19	
20	
23	
24	

Did you notice anything strange about the puzzles in the Graven End newspaper?

From Katie McCrawley's personal notebook:

This was brutal — smashing the lid down on the kid's neck severed his spinal cord immediately. At least it was quick and painless, which is a small mercy. I liked Josh. He always made sure my pizzas were delivered first so they were as hot as possible.

I don't quite understand the motive behind this one. The killer didn't like mushrooms on his pizza? Is that it? They must be fairly unhinged if that's all it takes to set them off. Also, the puzzles make it seem like they're taunting us, but to what end?

Hopefully it's a one off, but I have a feeling it isn't. Turner doesn't agree, but my gut is telling me this isn't the last puzzle we see. Need to go to the newsagent and grab a puzzle book. Brush up on my crosswords, just in case.

CRIME SCENE
<u>TWO</u>

LOCATION:
Inside the
academic library
at Graven End
University

MURDER WEAPON:
Monogrammed letter
opener

CONFIDENTIAL

VICTIM:
Daniel Jones

The victim was checking in and shelving a trolley full of new medical textbooks that had just come in from the printers.

Despite being deep in the stacks, it seems strange that he failed to hear the heavy wooden doors open or footsteps on the library's creaky wooden floor. It's been suggested by ████████ that ██.

The working theory is that the killer crept up behind the victim and stabbed him in the back with the victim's own letter opener, taken from the library's front desk.

As Detective McCrawley walks up the stairs to the university library, an officer waiting at the top hands her a piece of paper.

Hello, Detective McCrawley.

Can you work out where the body is?

I'll make it easy for you. It's in the only location listed in these library-themed anagrams.

casipnmurf

oilsfcstniacai

lietts

slhscroa

aidiflbrrn

Jhriscae

oxetbtkos

gnenldi

Transcript of conversation between Detective
Sergeant Katie McCrawley and Detective Constable
Alex Summers, conducted via text message.

Summers: U here?

McCrawley: Just walking over. Easton?

Summers: No. Don't need him. Killer's givn time
             of death?

McCrawley: k. What is it?

Summers: Oh. Um. Not sure yet?

McCrawley: ...

[END OF TRANSCRIPT]

When McCrawley arrived at the crime scene, Summers
hands her the following scrap of paper, with a shrug.

PUZZLE
28

Can you solve the following puzzle
and work out the time of death?

Two hours ago it was as long after
1 p.m. as it was before 1 a.m.

What time is it now?

47

Sara's PUZZLE PAGES

Arrow Words

PUZZLE 29

Not outside ▼	▼	Part of the eye ▼	▼	Eternal	Entice to do something ▼	Small storage rooms or cupboards ▼	Birthplace of St Francis ▼	Domestic animal ▼
Drink consumed before bed ▶		▼						
Dr ___: US record producer ▶				Otherwise ▶				
Viscous liquid ▶				Opposite of least ▶				
▶				23rd Greek letter ▶				Secret agent ▼
Garden watering device ▶		Meaning; purpose ▶		Daly: TV presenter ▶				
▶				Large ▶	Turn upside down ▶			
Egyptian goddess ▶	Female sheep (pl)		Conceal	▼	Jackie ___: famous actor		Public houses	
Principle of morality ▶	▼		▼		▼	Frozen water		Acquire ▼
Measuring heaviness ▶						▼		▼
Finish ▶				Spots ▶				
Sent rest (anag) ▶								

Behind every puzzle is a new mystery waiting to be uncovered.

PUZZLE
30

A- Z

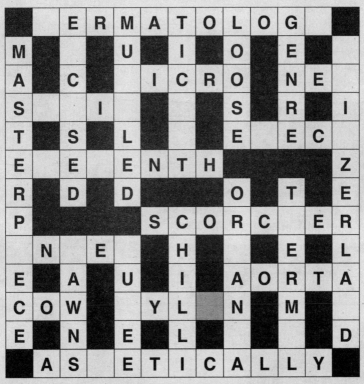

A B C D E F G H I J K L M N O P Q R S T U V W X Y Z

Once the body has been removed, McCrawley and Summers stood in the stacks, studying the location of the murder. It takes less than five minutes for them to spot that the books on the shelves behind where the victim's body had rested are not all medical texts. Notable, as they are standing in the medical section of the library.

Inviting the Storm

Climbing to the Top: How to Climb Your Own Mountain and Not Die

On Top of Tablewood Barn

Unreal: A Guide to the Formation of Kidney Stones

Long-tailed Invertebrates & Humanoid Robots

Determining Who, What, Why & When: The Art of Storytelling

How to Say Nothing in 500 Words

A Perfect Town: An Architect's Guide to Milton Keynes, UK

Visions: The Tomb in the Air

Eye of the Dragon

Buddhist Architecture of Awakening & the Cultural Changes

Evaluation Plans for Telemedicine

Environmental Magic - A Plant-based Witches Guide to Harnessing Power

Needed For Duty

Gender, Sexuality, Biomedicine, and HIV

Ramen 500 Ways

Electric Exile

A Research on Human Experiments Throughout the History of Mankind

The Codex Chrisicus

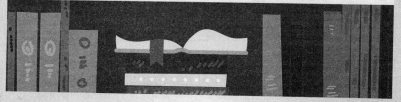

Can you spot anything special about these particular titles?

Sara's PUZZLE PAGES

Crossword

PUZZLE
32

Across

1 Person who looks identical to another (6,5)
9 Assembly of witches (5)
10 Trouble in body or mind (3)
11 Ethical (5)
12 Hermann ___ : author of Steppenwolf (5)
13 Unmarried woman (8)
16 Distance marker in a race (8)
18 ___ on: urged; encouraged (5)
21 Momentary oversight (5)
22 Not well (3)
23 Egg-shaped (5)
24 Pretentious display (11)

Down

2 Resistance to change (7)
3 Hermit (7)
4 Idolise (6)
5 Period of time lasting of 28-31 days (5)
6 Incites (5)
7 Creating an evocative mood (11)
8 Byword for the British Press (5,6)
14 Cause to deviate (7)
15 Underwater projectile (7)
17 Deposit knowledge (6)
19 Very strong winds (5)
20 Semiconductor (5)

Pathfinder: Famous Books

PUZZLE
33

S	I	R	A	L	C	R	I	A	F
S	I	X	O	T	O	B	Y	D	Y
A	U	O	D	E	M	Y	S	I	T
T	Q	N	S	L	I	B	K	C	I
H	E	S	E	O	N	T	H	A	N
I	G	S	Y	L	V	O	E	V	D
N	R	M	A	U	A	B	R	O	A
G	E	S	N	Y	R	E	M	A	D
O	O	C	Z	O	H	E	I	A	A
P	H	E	R	G	T	T	R	L	M

CLARISSA	MOBY-DICK	THE GINGER MAN
DON QUIXOTE	ON THE ROAD	THE TRIAL
HERZOG	SCOOP	ULYSSES
MADAME BOVARY	SYBIL	VANITY FAIR

You are capable of doing amazing puzzles.

During a search of the library's archives, a torn up piece of paper is found underneath one of the bookshelves. Can you piece it back together?

orm

PMI
s from

GRAVEN END UNIVERSITY

lds little value when applied
" (Sutherland, et al., 2003),
versial and widely accepted,
st-mortem reveals new ways of
o better assist law enforcement.

, cadaveric spasm, PMI

e can be caused by the cadaver
thed in a shirt or a well-
cket), and the condition of
pre-mortem (an emaciated
lated than an obese one).
t account for the pre-
of the cadaver, as
ut in the elements
nowy December
rnal temperature

Vol. 46 (4), 201
International Journal of Evi

**The key is in the stomach
estimations and methods
cad**

Leo
Department of Biolo
leo.san

Abstract: Currently, "PM
to human remains

4, pp. 465-472
dence-Based Justice Ref

davers
n - rethinking current
of taking temperature

Santana
ogy, Graven End University
tana@geu.edu

Keywords: thermoregula

1. INTRODUCTION

The body maintains a c
temperature of appro
(98.6°F), the optimum
the thousands of che
needed for life. As br
so does the cessatio
body functions. Th
which controls th
feature of thermoreg
function and the t

in re
but a review of the cur
of determining cadaveric t
calculating PMI estimatio

imately 37°C
temperature for
the cadaver F
body is less insu

It also does n
mortem temperature
someone who has been o
for hours during a s
would have a lower inte

estimation approach ho
l criminal investigation,
ent methods, both contro
emperature immediately pos
s, allowing forensic teams to

tion, soup, tissue dehydration

difference
being clo
insulated ja

temperature of
ion begins to rise,
bient temperature
h death occurred.
wn as algor mortis.
carried out by
in 2002, shows
a delay of up to
mortem before the
the cadaver begins
contrasts with the
ate of a 1°C (33.8°F)
r. Also, this accepted
oes not take into
factors: the position
(is it in the foetal
location (bodies in
ratures will reach an
equilibrium at a faster
e in humid climates),
f clothing (temperature

who had beer
the same period. Nev
Cooling is inefficient, a
can not be input into th
accuracy with which
temperature can currentl
remains less than is p
reliable forensic patholo

This article will l
methods that can be appli
in order to obtain a much
temperature at the time
gaining more knowledge
we will be able to offer
COD recommendations an
assistance to law enforcem

2. THE SOUP METHOD

One controversial but wide
of obtaining cadaveric tempe
soup method. The pathologist
(9 in) glass needle and careful

cadaver in question b
syncing with the an
of the area in whic
This cooling is kno

Research
Al-Alousi, et al.
that there can be
three hours post-
temperature of
to drop, which
widely accepted
decrease per hou
measurement d
account externa
of the cadaver
position?), the
subzero tempe
environmental
rate than thos
the presence c

indoors during
vton's Law of
as these factors
o the equation.
h post-mortem
y be calculated
referred for a
gical opinion.
ok at various
ed to cadavers
more accurate
of death. By
in this area,
more precise
d give better
ent officials.

ly used way
rature is the
uses a 23 cm
ly inserts it

Sara's PUZZLE PAGES

Codebreaker

PUZZLE 35

16	11	18	13	8	9	2	21	■	26	21	11	9
3	■	3	■	11	■	16	■	2	■	22	■	2
26	13	3	15	4	■	22	■	3	12	1	10	15
10	■	1	■	4	■	1	■	1	■	5	■	22
■	■	■	7	10	4	4	22	26	3	1	10	5
1	■	10	■	15	■	20	■	10	■	10	■	22
10	6	13	3	26	10	■	13	15	10	26	10	4
12	■	22	■	2	■	15	■	17	■	26	■	23
2	3	14	14	3	25	11	22	9	14	■	■	■
3	■	3	■	4	■	26	■	4	■	18	■	24
18	9	19	22	2	■	26	■	3	15	22	8	22
10	■	11	■	16	■	22	■	15	■	1	■	1
15	10	10	21	■	14	9	5	23	14	22	21	10

A B C D E F G H I J K L M N O P Q R S T U V W X Y Z

1	2	3	4	5	6	7	8	9	10	11	12	13
									E			P

14	15	16	17	18	19	20	21	22	23	24	25	26
							K					

<u>Word Search: Countries of Europe</u>

PUZZLE
36

Y	D	L	Z	I	A	R	Y	L	X	Z	D	L	C	L
X	I	R	E	L	A	N	D	N	A	L	O	P	S	T
W	L	F	B	U	L	G	A	R	I	A	L	S	P	P
Y	R	C	N	X	C	A	Y	D	F	T	L	K	A	A
C	A	C	Z	E	C	H	R	E	P	U	B	L	I	C
O	Y	W	L	M	T	E	R	N	K	P	C	A	N	C
H	X	P	R	B	E	H	I	M	M	R	E	G	A	E
V	M	V	R	O	A	I	E	A	E	A	U	U	I	B
S	L	U	A	U	N	P	L	R	V	I	S	T	K	T
F	C	A	I	R	S	T	K	K	L	T	E	R	A	I
R	H	U	N	G	A	R	Y	L	R	A	C	O	V	X
S	X	M	N	I	L	D	R	I	B	O	N	P	O	P
S	G	R	E	E	C	E	A	I	L	R	A	D	L	E
T	M	R	P	S	T	A	B	M	L	C	R	T	S	T
U	D	E	S	G	N	E	D	E	W	S	F	K	M	Y

AUSTRIA	FRANCE	NORWAY
BELGIUM	GREECE	POLAND
BULGARIA	HUNGARY	PORTUGAL
CROATIA	IRELAND	SLOVAKIA
CYPRUS	LUXEMBOURG	SPAIN
CZECH REPUBLIC	MALTA	SWEDEN
DENMARK	NETHERLANDS	TURKEY

Stack #42

One among these seven holds the answer you crave.
And there's a clue in the answer, and a life you
could save.
The tome you're after is neither short, nor tall.
Its title has just letters and no numbers at all.
You won't find it at the start, the middle, or end.
And when looking for answers, food isn't your friend.
The category is fiction, because fantasy is best.
So books about real people won't help in this quest.
Finally, the story's about magic, knights and of mages.
Understand, there are no feathers betwixt
these pages.

One of the Crime Scene Techs hands McCrawley a piece of
paper that has been found in the bin beside the library's
front desk, where the victim had been working.

Can you use the riddle on the left and the photo below to work out which of the books the killer is directing us to?

Poisons of the Andes

What Sarah Did Next: 40 ways to improve your health through eating gravy

The Elephant's Castle

Around the World in 80 Stinky Cheeses

Telephone Numbers of New Jersey - 1998

The Girl with the Hummingbird Tattoo

A Scandalous History of Madame Blanket & London's Second-Best Brothel

Sara's PUZZLE PAGES

THE BEST-SELLING NEWSPAPER IN GRAVEN END

Letter-Doku!

PUZZLE 38

	B			A				
		D		G	B	A		
F	D				E		G	
H	F	D	G		A	C		
		I	F		D	G	B	H
	E		H				C	G
	G	B	E		F			
				G			F	

A new one for you today, fellow puzzlers. This is just like regular sudoku, but I've replaced the numbers 1–9 with the letters A–I. Easy-peasy.

Sara x

Crossword

PUZZLE
39

Across

1 Makes a garment from wool (5)
4 Skilled job (5)
10 Dignified conduct (7)
11 Tycoon (5)
12 Destroy (4)
13 Taking to be true (8)
16 Detects; feels (6)
17 Put on a production (6)
20 False impression (8)
21 Cut (4)
23 Single seed of a cereal (5)
25 Flight hub (7)
26 Unwanted plants (5)
27 Amplify a signal (5)

Down

2 Active at night (9)
3 Period of imprisonment (4)
5 Gets back on a horse (8)
6 Mist (3)
7 Loves dearly (6)
8 Entertain (5)
9 Stop up a hole (4)
14 Unsuspecting; innocent (9)
15 Diminished (8)
18 Repositories (6)
19 Pertaining to the sun (5)
20 Canines (4)
22 Bond movie (2,2)
24 Affirmative vote (3)

Written in pencil inside the front cover of *The Elephant's Castle* is a note to turn to "page 394". A codeword puzzle has been pasted onto the page.

The Elephant turned to the girl and laughed. "There's
...de to help a huge, rare

nothin...
elepha...
Who i...

talk a...
she sa...
you is...
well,
eleph...

eat a...
scre...
girl
don...
"Sh...
I ne...
cri...
the...
he...
pu...

26		6		20				5		8		16
8	6	13	13	15	21		25	1		18	22	6	1
15		22		22		12		17		6		6
20	6	3	6	9	22	6		22	3	7	4	19
20		23		22		22		25		19		21
22	10	6	12		6	11	4	4	24			
18		21		24		21		10		9		26
			25	4	6	2	21		18	8	22	6
21		11		13		18		20		22		11
26	18	6	2	8		4	7	22	18	6	9	2
22		2		4		12		6		2		14
6	21	8	4	18	22		6	9	9	22	23	22
18		22		3				8		23		21

A B C D E F G H I J K L M N O P Q R S T U V W X Y Z

1	2	3	4	5	6	7	8	9	10	11	12	13
1	1	N	1					2	3	1		

14	15	16	17	18	19	20	21	22	23	24	25	26
	2		K	1		P		2	2	1		

book

"No!" cried the girl. "That's not tru... ...you and your family. He feeds you and brings you treats, and bathes your wounds. He doesn't care if you can carry people around or not, just as long as you are happy and safe."

McCrawley thinks that the killer is leading them towards the title of a book they've probably come across before. Do you agree?

Anagram
Numbers - how many times a letter is used?

Sara's PUZZLE PAGES

THE BEST-SELLING NEWSPAPER IN GRAVEN END

Arrow Words

PUZZLE 42

Piece of code to automate a task	Area of land	Make less miserable	Kingdom	Sphere or globe	Lacking knowledge	▼	Type of bus (6-6)	▼
▶	▼	▼	▼		Sticky substance	▶		
US pop star ▶					Marine flatfish		Wireless	
Assimilate again ▶					▼		▼	
Slippery fish ▶			By word of mouth	▶				
▶								
Jellylike citrus preserve ▶		Large deer	Smell	Blyton: writer	▶			
▶		▼	▼	Makes a mistake	Foot extremity	▶		
Short note	Lyric poems ▶					Pay (anag)	Shola — singer	
Barrier between rooms ▶					Wild ox	▶	▼	
Ales ▶	Eg Jones or Smith ▶							
▶					Level golf score	▶		

Kriss Kross

PUZZLE 43

3 letters
Sec
Yet

4 letters
Help
Tack

5 letters
Carve
Nanny
Pilot
Stray

6 letters
Entrap
Greens
Ironic
Prises
Sample
Slalom

7 letters
Annexes
Compute
Concept
Lasagne
Skidded
Smelled
Studied
Wattage

8 letters
Ailments
Anaconda
Ballpark
Clarinet
Littoral
Predator

9 letters
Authentic
Developed

A library assistant explains that the library holds over 300 different copies of *The Codex Chrisicus*, and there are around 298 in stock, which is too many to search efficiently. When McCrawley types the title into the system, a screen with the following puzzle appears.

6	2	9	7	8	3	5	6	7	9	9	1	6	9	9	9780908827483
6	7	3	9	4	6	8	9	2	7	2	9	1	7	0	9781827349789
9	3	9	7	8	0	9	0	8	8	2	7	4	8	3	9782318244980
7	7	7	8	1	2	7	9	7	5	5	8	8	6	7	9782667743201
8	8	8	3	5	8	8	1	6	6	3	3	7	7	4	9783310063426
0	9	1	5	6	4	2	8	5	9	2	3	9	9	2	9781577353025
9	7	8	9	8	8	6	5	3	8	2	1	2	0	1	9783596800739
8	0	2	6	9	7	6	2	4	7	3	0	7	6	6	9781167588211
6	9	7	8	1	5	7	7	3	5	3	0	2	5	7	9784677834221
5	2	3	0	3	5	7	7	3	4	9	6	3	3	9	9783567991699
3	5	4	0	8	9	4	3	2	3	9	3	4	5	0	9785698754323
5	6	9	7	8	2	3	1	8	2	4	4	9	8	0	9786790653588
6	7	7	3	1	4	2	6	1	3	0	2	6	8	6	9789850564367
9	7	8	9	8	5	0	5	6	4	3	6	7	9	7	9789886538212
9	1	9	7	8	1	1	6	7	5	8	8	2	1	1	

Can you find the ISBN of a particular copy of the Codex Chrisicus that the killer is pointing you towards?

The Codex Chrisicus

Page number?

Summers locates the book first and brings it to
McCrawley. When asked why he had failed to complete
the puzzle pasted on the cover, his response is:
"I can't do sudokus. Too many numbers".

Sara's PUZZLE PAGES

THE BEST-SELLING NEWSPAPER IN GRAVEN END

A-Z

PUZZLE
46

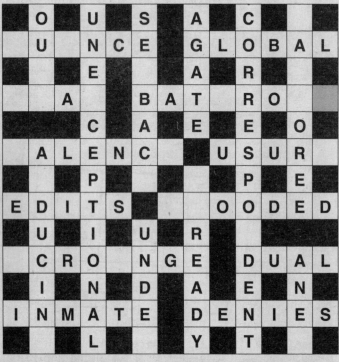

	O		U		S		A		C			
	U		N	C	E		G	L	O	B	A	L
			E				A		R			
		A			B	A	T		R	O		
			C		A		E		E		O	
A	L	E	N	C			U	S	U	R		
			P					P		E		
E	D	I	T	S			O	O	D	E	D	
U		I		U		R						
C	R	O		N	G	E		D	U	A	L	
I		N		D		A		E		N		
I	N	M	A	T	E		D	E	N	I	E	S
		L				Y		T				

A B C D E F G H I J K L M N O P Q R S T U V W X Y Z

— ❝ —

Even the hardest puzzle has a solution.

— ❞ —

Pathfinder: The Good Ol' USA

H	O	H	I	T	E	U	S	E	L
N	L	W	E	R	H	O	U	O	A
O	L	Y	W	O	S	U	N	M	S
T	G	O	O	M	H	R	T	I	V
I	N	D	E	S	S	A	R	M	E
H	S	F	M	I	Q	U	E	A	G
W	A	L	A	T	O	F	M	I	A
S	E	O	D	N	R	I	L	H	S
E	L	R	I	I	A	C	A	O	U
G	N	A	S	O	L	N	O	T	S

CALIFORNIA   LAS VEGAS   MOUNT RUSHMORE
FLORIDA   LOS ANGELES   TIMES SQUARE
HOLLYWOOD   MIAMI   WASHINGTON
HOUSTON   WHITE HOUSE

Hello amateur Enigmatologists! Hope you've enjoyed this week's puzzles. Just reminding you that there will be no puzzles for the rest of the week. I'm off to Puzzleby for a murder mystery weekend. See you next week!

Sara x

On page 194, there is another puzzle glued onto the page.

You didn't think it would be that easy, did you? Perhaps it's on this page?

37				33			3		
		41	76				1		6
			96		88	79			8
43		○	97					29	
			100	98	91				11
		72	93		85			27	
46		70	71		83				
				65	64	60		20	
48	52								15
			55	56	23				

Partial email conversation between Detective Sergeant McCrawley and Doctor Alan Easton

FROM: Dr. Alan Easton <a.easton@gravenlaboratory.com>
TO: Det. Katie McCrawley <kmcrawley@ge-police.com>

Re: Quick question!

Katie,

I did go to Graven End's own illustrious university, but that was many moons ago and I was a completely different person back then.

I guess I must have run into Daniel Jones somewhere around the campus but, like I said, it was so long ago now.

Sorry I couldn't be more helpful. Do let me know if there's anything else I help with (or not help with, as the case may be).

Best,

Alan

TUES 18/04/2020 09:58

FROM: Det. Katie McCrawley <kmcrawley@ge-police.com>
TO: Dr. Alan Easton <a.easton@gravenlaboratory.com>

Quick question!

Alan,

You went to GE Uni back in the day, right? Is there any chance you knew the victim? We were just following up on a few leads when I remembered you went there possibly around the same time as the victim.

Sara's PUZZLE PAGES

THE BEST-SELLING NEWSPAPER IN GRAVEN END

Hello again, amateur Enigmatologists! Thanks to everyone who asked about my murder mystery weekend. It was a blast! I had a great time but I am back and raring to go with some new, tricky puzzles.

Sara x

PUZZLE
49

Word search: Book Characters

ANNA KARENINA
ATTICUS FINCH
CHARLIE BUCKET
CINDERELLA
ELINOR DASHWOOD
FRODO BAGGINS
GANDALF
HARRY POTTER
JANE BENNET
JAY GATSBY
JULIET
MAD HATTER
MARY CRAWFORD
MATILDA
MISS TRUNCHBULL
PETER PAN
QUEEN OF HEARTS
ROMEO
SLEEPING BEAUTY
SNOW WHITE
WILLY WONKA

E	G	S	T	T	A	K	N	O	W	Y	L	L	I	W
Q	B	L	M	E	G	A	N	D	A	L	F	L	Q	T
P	F	E	A	K	H	Y	Q	R	A	A	Z	U	O	E
A	R	E	R	C	C	X	H	E	N	T	E	B	E	I
Y	O	P	Y	U	I	L	C	T	I	E	T	H	M	L
B	D	I	C	B	N	M	N	T	N	N	I	C	O	U
S	O	N	R	E	D	A	I	O	E	N	H	N	R	J
T	B	G	A	I	E	D	F	P	R	E	W	U	A	N
A	A	B	W	L	R	H	S	Y	A	B	W	R	D	A
G	G	E	F	R	E	A	U	R	K	E	O	T	L	P
Y	G	A	O	A	L	T	C	R	A	N	N	S	I	R
A	I	U	R	H	L	T	I	A	N	A	S	S	T	E
J	N	T	D	C	A	E	T	H	N	J	A	I	A	T
S	S	Y	Z	I	R	R	T	X	A	D	N	M	M	E
E	L	I	N	O	R	D	A	S	H	W	O	O	D	P

Codebreaker

PUZZLE 50

	20		10		5		15		5		4	
6	10	26	3	23	18		22	21	17	15	22	7
	22		26		15		19		15		26	
1	7	3	2		13	22	10	11	8	26	15	17
			23		25		26		25		11	
5	21	11	26	21	3	26		8	1	21	8	5
	13		4		19		9		25		1	
16	21	1	17	5		20	21	10	5	17	26	22
	11		25		11		22		15			
11	26	5	21	12	21	25	23		17	25	23	14
	17		3		21		26		25		22	
22	26	17	15	25	3		4	18	21	17	21	3
	22		1		5		5		3		24	

A B C D E F G H I J K L M N O P Q R S T U V W X Y Z

1	2	3	4	5	6	7	8	9	10	11	12	13
								F				

14	15	16	17	18	19	20	21	22	23	24	25	26
	A									W		

A search is conducted for the specific copy of the Codex Chrisicus with the ISBN 9784677834221. Upon removing the book from the shelf, a piece of paper flutters out.

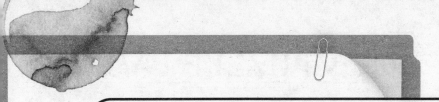

Officer Gibson finds a translation of the Codex.
Can you decode the message left by the killer?

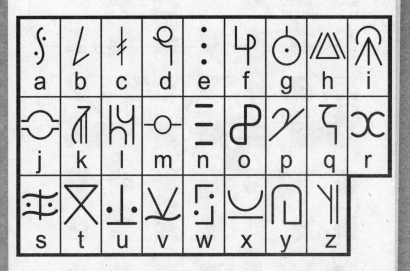

a	b	c	d	e	f	g	h	i
j	k	l	m	n	o	p	q	r
s	t	u	v	w	x	y	z	

Sara's PUZZLE PAGES

Crossword

PUZZLE
52

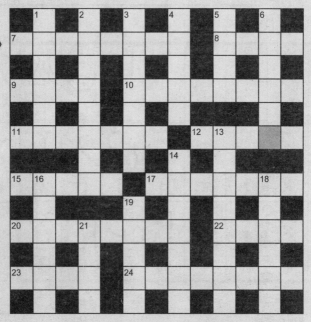

Across

7 Peacemaker (8)
8 Cereal grains (4)
9 Passionate desire for something (4)
10 Lacking knowledge (8)
11 Safe places (7)
12 Inferior to (5)
15 Religious groups (5)
17 Go backwards (7)
20 Muttered (8)
22 River in central England (4)
23 Not as much (4)
24 State of being the same (8)

Down

1 Coniferous tree (6)
2 Cause deliberate damage to (8)
3 Hopes to achieve (7)
4 Main stem of a tree (5)
5 Not sweet (4)
6 Causes a sharp pain (6)
13 Capable of being used (8)
14 Necessary (7)
16 Displayed freely (6)
18 Fires a bullet (6)
19 Small container (5)
21 Sentimentality (4)

> Everything you need is right in front of you. You need only pay attention.

A-Z

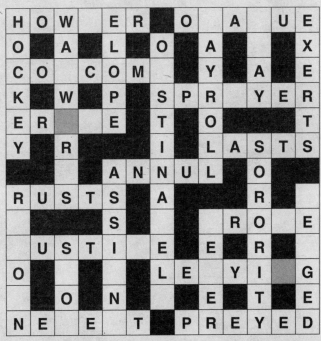

H	O	W		E	R		O		A		U	E
O		A		L		O		A				X
C	O		C	O	M			Y		A		E
K		W		P		S	P	R		Y	E	R
E	R			E		T		O				T
Y		R			I		L	A	S	T	S	
			A	N	N	U	L		O			
R	U	S	T	S		A			R			
		S					R	O			E	
	U	S	T	I		E		E		R		
O				L	E		Y	I				G
		O		N			E		T			E
N	E		E		T		P	R	E	Y	E	D

A B C D E F G H I J K L M N O P Q R S T U V W X Y Z

McCrawley knows that the murder weapon – a monogrammed letter opener – was taken from the victim's desk near the entrance to the archives. She obtains CCTV stills from the camera that overlooks the entrance.

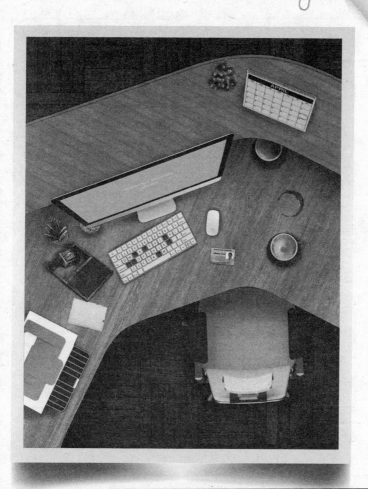

An additional photo is taken by the Crime Scene Techs. Did the killer change or alter the desk? Can you determine all **ten** differences between the two photographs?

Use this page to record any notes or answers for this crime. This may help you to determine who you think the killer is at the very end.

PUZZLE	ANSWER
27	
28	
31	
34	
37	
40	
41	
44	
45	
48	
51	
54	

Did you notice anything strange about the puzzles in the Graven End newspaper?

I tempted fate! I should've known not to write about this being a "one off". However, good to know I can trust my gut, still.

Stabbed in the back with his own letter opener. Is that suggestive of the killer's mindset? Payback for being metaphorically stabbed in the back? This murder definitely seemed like the killer was getting revenge. Did Jones and the killer have a history?

The killer seems to be having fun with the puzzles this time, getting into their stride. I wish I knew what their endgame was. It's like they're showing us how smart they are.

But why???

CRIME SCENE
THREE

LOCATION:
The One-Stop-Pop-
And-Shop car park,
Dawes Close

MURDER WEAPON:
The victim's own
walking stick

ELEMENTS OF THE FILE HAVE BEEN
REDACTED DUE TO THE HIGHLY CONFIDENTIAL
NATURE OF THE CASE. THE FILE AND
CONTENTS ARE THE PROPERTY OF THE GRAVEN END
POLICE DEPARTMENT. REMOVAL FROM THE
BUILDING WILL RESULT IN IMMEDIATE ARREST.

VICTIM:
Hetty Merryweather

Sixteen days before the victim was found in the supermarket car park, beaten to death with her own walking stick, she had been part of an altercation in the same car park.

The victim had pulled out of a parking space without looking and driven into the side of an in-motion car. It was a low-speed collision, but she refused to take any blame for the incident, or hand over insurance details, leaving the other driver to pay for repairs out of pocket.

Further investigation uncovered that the victim was eighty-nine years old and had been banned from driving for the past seven months. Neighbours also described her as an ▓▓▓▓▓▓▓▓▓▓▓▓▓▓▓▓▓▓▓▓▓▓▓▓▓▓▓▓ who was not very ▓▓▓▓▓▓▓▓▓▓▓▓▓▓▓▓▓▓▓▓▓▓▓▓▓▓.

Sara's PUZZLE PAGES

THE BEST-SELLING NEWSPAPER IN GRAVEN END

Word Search: Bowling Fun

PUZZLE 55

A	M	T	T	N	D	I	R	I	A	A	Q	T	V	G
E	R	I	A	Q	W	O	S	U	Q	T	F	M	C	I
R	C	L	B	T	V	W	U	U	T	O	I	O	S	N
I	N	P	O	C	K	E	T	B	M	T	T	F	J	S
F	L	S	B	H	O	O	K	F	L	U	S	H	D	X
B	I	E	R	U	O	F	G	I	B	E	B	T	G	V
R	A	O	O	C	K	T	O	A	R	T	A	F	A	M
P	R	C	O	E	U	X	H	I	K	T	S	I	S	Q
J	H	H	K	O	L	S	E	C	O	P	S	N	I	P
A	S	Q	L	E	E	S	G	Z	A	F	L	A	E	T
P	U	L	Y	Q	N	F	D	R	S	O	P	O	X	I
I	O	L	N	R	N	D	E	B	F	U	R	T	U	X
R	O	H	C	N	A	A	H	T	F	L	A	P	A	E
S	W	O	C	V	H	T	U	D	M	A	T	A	P	B
R	S	W	U	C	C	S	S	T	Z	A	U	R	P	A

ANCHOR	DOUBLE	POCKET
APPROACH	FLUSH	RAIL
BACK END	FOUL	ROLL-OUT
BIG FOUR	HEDGEHOG	SERIES
BROOKLYN	HOOK	SPARE
CHANNEL	LOFT	SPLIT
CHOP	PINS	STRIKE

Crossword

Across

1 Slender freshwater fish (4)
3 Opera texts (8)
9 Devoted time to learning (7)
10 Small farm (5)
11 Moved quickly on foot (3)
12 A written document (5)
13 Upright (5)
15 Loutish person (5)
17 Solemn promises (5)
18 23rd Greek letter (3)
19 Declare invalid (5)
20 Giving the ball to another team member (7)
21 Boating (8)
22 Large group of people (4)

Down

1 Available for use as needed; optional (13)
2 Stir milk (5)
4 One of the halogens (6)
5 Person who receives office visitors (12)
6 Groups of actors (7)
7 Fascinatingly (13)
8 As quickly as possible (7-5)
14 Of great size (7)
16 Occur (6)
18 Cost (5)

PUZZLE
56

A word search is found carefully placed on the
victim's forehead, and the Crime Scene Techs find
a receipt in her car. The detectives need to know
if the types of food the victim purchased on the day
of her murder match those found in the word search.

A	P	P	L	E	S	Y	V	H	G	R	A	P	E	S
T	U	L	M	P	S	T	N	P	F	A	W	Z	N	Q
Q	B	A	T	T	U	X	O	E	S	E	A	I	Z	A
H	H	M	B	U	T	T	E	R	T	T	S	T	U	N
K	L	B	L	U	E	B	E	R	R	I	E	S	D	O
Z	L	F	Z	F	Z	P	R	I	A	A	T	E	Y	M
Z	N	E	K	C	I	H	C	R	W	A	C	I	G	U
T	O	L	X	G	Z	E	H	D	B	L	H	R	L	T
E	A	T	O	S	C	B	O	X	E	L	E	R	L	R
L	S	T	S	A	L	A	C	H	R	R	E	E	T	J
U	A	A	K	Q	F	C	O	S	R	Y	S	B	K	A
D	A	E	R	B	T	O	L	P	I	T	E	P	M	S
A	S	S	A	N	A	N	A	B	E	N	G	S	Z	L
L	C	K	S	X	L	P	T	O	S	J	G	A	A	S
I	R	U	I	S	S	E	E	B	H	G	S	R	O	S

ONE-STOP-POP-AND-SHOP
Dawes Close, Graven End

CASHIER: MARINA

APPLES	£0.49
BACON	£1.89
BANANAS	£0.98
BEEF	£11.29
BLUEBERRIES	£2.09
BREAD	£0.89
BUTTER	£1.25
CARROTS	£0.99
CHEESE	£3.26
CHICKEN	£4.19
CHOCOLATE	£1.49
EGGS	£1.89
GRAPES	£2.79
HAM	£1.69
LAMB	£15.63
LEEKS	£2.09
NUTS	£1.99
RAISINS	£1.63
RASPBERRIES	£2.19
RICE CAKES	£2.55
STRAWBERRIES	£1.79

TOTAL: £63.05

PAYMENT METHOD: CARD
TRANSACTION #153326577

DATE: 12/6/2020 2:06:14 PM
THANK YOU

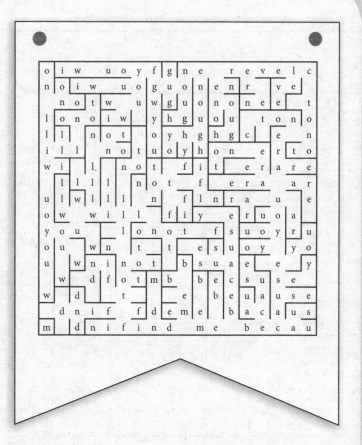

The Crime Scene Techs discover some bunting between the trees in the car park. There are multiple routes in this puzzle, but only one is correct. If you can find the correct path, you will reveal a message left behind by the killer. The first word in the killer's message is YOU.

Sara's PUZZLE PAGES

Kriss Kross

PUZZLE 59

3 letters
Ask
Cub
Ear
Met
Sag
Sup
Tau

4 letters
Auks
Case
Gape
Ibis
Ohms
Sash
Scud
Tans
Uses
Yoga

5 letters
Cowed
Emery

6 letters
Drives
Thence

7 letters
Cantata
Infuses
Muddied
Roofing
Skidded
Stimuli
Towpath
Yttrium

8 letters
Currents
Minstrel
Obduracy
Platform

9 letters
Oscillate
Woodchuck

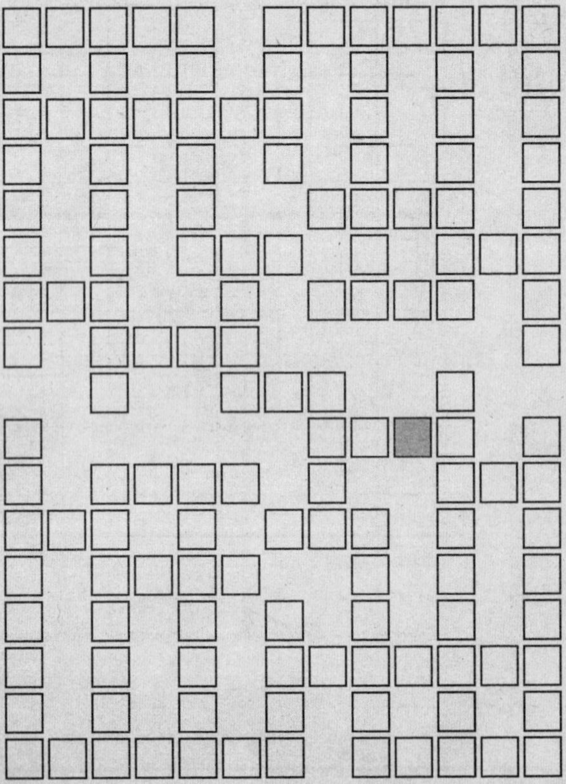

Letter-Doku!

PUZZLE 60

			B				A	E
				F		G		
		A					F	H
E				B				
F	D	B				I	H	C
				C				A
D	E				A			
		F		I				
	B	I			H			

There are a lot of footprints on the ground at the crime scene, but McCrawley notices that one set doesn't match the samples they've collected from witnesses and staff. Can you find the set that doesn't match?

1.

Chris Parris
Crime Scene
Technician

2.

Marina May
Owner of the
One-Stop-Pop-
and-Stop

3.

PC Sam Wick
First officer
on the scene

4.

**Sergeant Amy
Bryant**
Officer on
scene

5.

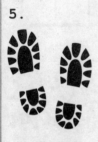

Rich Mills
Bystander

6.

**Detective
Sergeant Kate
McCrawley**

7.

Jason Gacey
The teen who
found the body

8.

**Hetty
Merryweather**
Victim

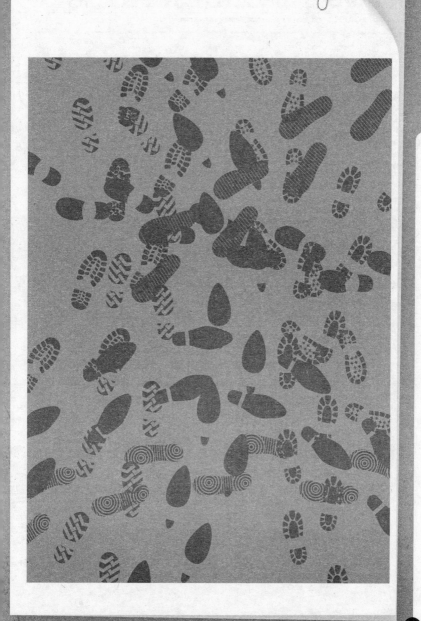

Sara's PUZZLE PAGES

THE BEST-SELLING NEWSPAPER IN GRAVEN END

Pathfinder: Mammal Madness!

PUZZLE 62

T	A	C	E	L	O	P	R	E	G
W	R	C	T	E	G	O	A	T	I
O	A	C	I	L	P	O	E	O	T
L	F	F	V	O	A	R	L	X	E
F	X	O	T	N	C	D	N	E	E
E	E	L	H	A	H	I	A	N	Z
R	O	E	P	H	I	M	P	K	B
R	O	G	N	C	P	M	U	N	E
E	R	A	A	K	N	O	B	R	A
T	C	A	M	E	L	S	I	E	V

ARCTIC FOX	CHIPMUNK	OXEN
BEAVER	ELEPHANT	POLECAT
BISON	FERRET	TIGER
CAMEL	GOAT	VOLE
CHIMPANZEE	KANGAROO	WOLF
	LEOPARD	

> Like people, some puzzles aren't what they seem. You have to look deeper.

A - Z

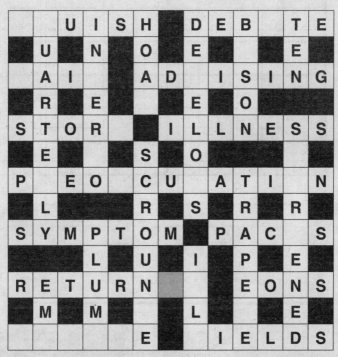

A B C D E F G H I J K L M N O P Q R S T U V W X Y Z

				1				28	
		9			97	100	33	32	
7			23		99				
13	15			95					
	17				89	90			
	20		62	87		85	81	72	
	59		77		79				
			76						39
		57	65		68		46	44	
53		51							41

When the footprints are identified, Detective McCrawley notices that there is a trail of them around the car park. Can you use the Journeys puzzle an officer finds in the bin to work out the killer's route in and out of the car park?

After Dr. Easton and his team have taken the victim's body back to the Graven End laboratory for further tests, a search of the immediate area finds no trace of the victim's car. The officers on the scene discover a piece of paper slipped under the windscreen wiper of a car on the far side of the car park.

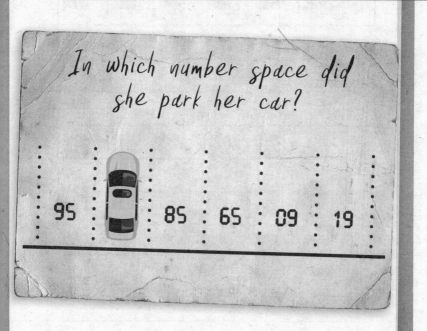

In which number space did she park her car?

95　　85　65　09　19

Can you work out in what number space the victim's car is parked?

Sara's PUZZLE PAGES

THE BEST-SELLING NEWSPAPER IN GRAVEN END

Codebreaker

PUZZLE 66

8		13		14				15		2		5
24	19	12	13	9	4		14	24	25	10	11	1
13		6		17		10		8		7		9
22	10	5	1	13	5	26		3	5	7	24	24
10		13		20		15		12		4		6
5	10	22	12		16	17	10	20	18			
9		18		15		22		18		8		9
			18	21	12	12	20		23	17	22	24
18		18		5		11		2		20		17
26	24	20	24	13		8	5	23	24	9	12	22
10		5		5		12		24		5		12
9	12	18	18	24	11		12	13	5	18	12	18
12		21		21				22		18		20

A B C D E F G H I J K L M N O P Q R S T U V W X Y Z

1	2	3	4	5	6	7	8	9	10	11	12	13
			Y				**C**	**L**				

14	15	16	17	18	19	20	21	22	23	24	25	26

Arrow Words

PUZZLE
67

Possess	Sticky yellowish substance	▼	Small arm of the sea	Young men	Type of word puzzle	Garment maker	Liberties	▼
►			Coming after ▼	▼	▼	▼		
Mammal related to the llama							Document allowing entry to a country ▼	
►			Propel forwards ►					
Sharp chopping implement	Series of subject lessons		Of definite shape ►					
Desert in northern China	▼	Study of the past	▼	Mediocre (2-2)				
►				Public transport vehicle				
Etiquette		Sharif: Egyptian actor ▼		Look at amorously ▼		E.g. Shrek ▼	Princess ___: Star Wars character ▼	
►								Auction item ▼
Type of air pollution ►					Come together ►			
►					___ Ferdinand: England footballer ►			
Jewel from an oyster shell	Cereal plant ►				Consume food ►			

There are multiple tyre tracks around the area the body was found. Using the tyre print taken of the victim's car, can you determine if any of the tyre tracks match the victim's, so that the officers can work out if the killer moved her car after she was killed?

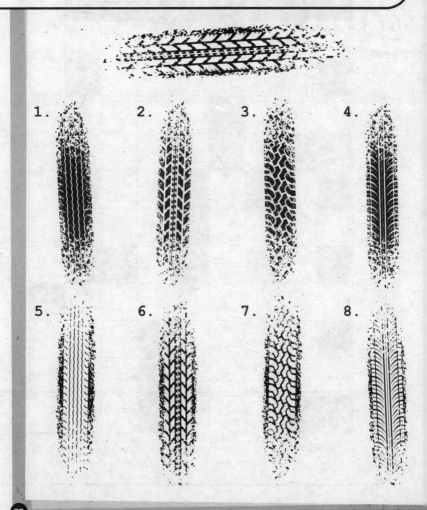

1.   2.   3.   4.

5.   6.   7.   8.

The New Gra

Friday, 18th June 2021

Murder in the Car Park

Ex-schoolteacher and town elder, Hetty Merryweather, was found dead n the car prk of the Graven End One-Stop Pop-and-Shop late onday night

Whilst investigations are still on-going, detetives beieve that Merryweather, 89, was struck ver the head repeatedly with her own walk-ing stick, which was found a hort distanc away fom he body.

Police are appealing to anyone who may have been in the sop or in the cr park at the time of the murder to come forward. Marina May, owner of the One-Stop-Pop-and-Shop, cofirmed that the CCTV cameras that cover the car park were vandalised last month and had not been repaired b the time f the mrder.

I is not known if te beloved ex-headmstress kew her attacer, or if it was a crime of opportunity.

The evening after the murder, Sara Dougherty, the enigmatologist from *The New Graven End News*, catches up with McCrawley and hands her an article torn out of the paper. "I noticed this was printed in today's issue. There's something strange about it".

Sara's PUZZLE PAGES

Kriss Kross

PUZZLE 70

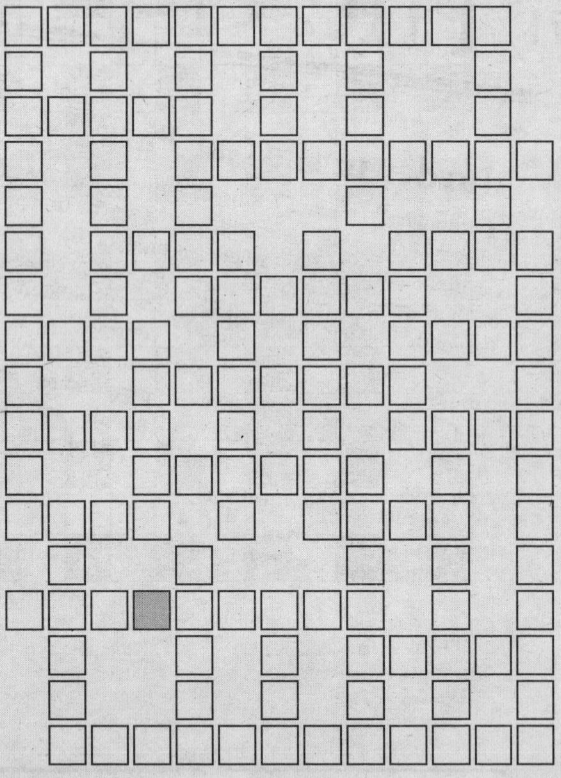

4 letters
Anon
Aura
Garb
Gods
Hire
Inns
Puma
Rump
Sari
Seer

5 letters
Adieu
Anger
Hopes
Inane
Noses
Stash

6 letters
Divest
Easter
Eclair
Outwit

7 letters
Bigness
Custard
Omnibus
Pebbles
Retsina

8 letters
Arpeggio
Irritant

9 letters
Standards
Tradesman

12 letters
Inadequately
Triumphantly
Unacceptable
Unhesitating

Crossword

PUZZLE 71

Across

7 Backward-looking (13)
8 Not extreme (8)
9 Scarce (4)
10 Framework (7)
12 Obscure road (5)
14 Later (5)
16 Foot pedal (7)
19 Pile (4)
20 Thing used for tying (8)
22 Easy to deal with (13)

Down

1 Short note or reminder (4)
2 Silver (literary) (6)
3 With an attitude of suspicion (7)
4 Number of deadly sins (5)
5 Tempestuous (6)
6 Take to pieces to examine (8)
11 In the open air (8)
13 Army unit (7)
15 Give a job to (6)
17 Sagacious (6)
18 Purple fruits (5)
21 Payment to a landlord (4)

Transcript of conversation between Detective Sergeant Katie McCrawley and Detective Constable Alex Summers, conducted via text message.

McCrawley: Before u come to the scene can u bring the metal detector, plz

Summers: where is it??

McCrawley: Charlton was playing with it last. ask him.

Summers: will do. why?

McCrawley: found the car but no key. Easton's office said there was no key in vic's belongings

Summers: cant u just bust the door?

McCrawley: No, the Crime Scene Techs dont want to in case they damage "vital evidence".

Summers: oh

McCrawley: yes. exactly. so we go key-hunting with the detector. Found it?

Summers: Charlton said he gave it to Nielson last Tuesday. Don't know where she is

McCrawley: ur a detective. Go detect her. and some coffee. black, 2 sugars, plz. Dont take too long. its cold and I want to go home sometime tonight

[END OF TRANSCRIPT]

A search with the metal detector finds a bunch of identical looking keys underneath a nearby car. Can you match the correct key to the lock and save any potential evidence?

Victim's car key:

Sara's PUZZLE PAGES

THE BEST-SELLING NEWSPAPER IN GRAVEN END

Letter-Doku!

PUZZLE
73

C								G
	I	F				B		
	E			D		F		
			B	F			D	
		B	H		I	C		
	H			A	D			
		C		E			B	
		D				E	C	
A								F

"

In life, each puzzle we tackle fulfils a larger goal. It's up to you to discover that goal.

"

Word Search: Oscar-Winning Films

PUZZLE
74

O	U	T	O	F	A	F	R	I	C	A	O	O	R	I
D	Y	N	Q	A	H	S	H	T	I	C	E	N	O	G
L	S	R	A	W	R	A	T	S	S	K	V	T	R	O
C	V	U	M	Y	Y	K	H	I	U	J	E	H	E	I
U	F	H	A	D	G	X	E	L	M	P	T	E	P	N
C	O	N	D	A	I	R	S	S	F	I	U	W	M	G
O	R	E	E	L	J	C	T	R	O	H	O	A	E	M
R	R	B	U	R	H	A	I	E	D	D	B	T	T	Y
P	E	G	S	I	T	T	N	L	N	N	A	E	S	W
A	S	R	C	A	E	O	G	D	U	A	L	R	A	A
T	T	A	I	F	R	O	A	N	O	G	L	F	L	Y
T	G	V	I	Y	A	K	M	I	S	I	A	R	E	S
O	U	I	O	M	B	S	D	H	E	G	V	O	H	K
N	M	T	I	T	A	N	I	C	H	I	R	N	T	K
S	P	Y	O	P	C	S	W	S	T	X	N	T	K	Z

ALL ABOUT EVE	GIGI	PATTON
AMADEUS	GOING MY WAY	SCHINDLER'S LIST
BEN-HUR	GRAVITY	STAR WARS
CABARET	MY FAIR LADY	THE LAST EMPEROR
CHICAGO	ON THE WATERFRONT	THE SOUND OF MUSIC
FORREST GUMP	OUT OF AFRICA	THE STING
GANDHI		TITANIC

Using the key, officers finally manage to open the boot
of the victim's car. A photo of the victim's boot is
sitting on top of her things.

Can you compare it to a photo taken by the Crime Scene Techs and see if anything has changed? There are **six** differences between the two photographs.

Sara's PUZZLE PAGES

THE BEST-SELLING NEWSPAPER IN GRAVEN END

A - Z

PUZZLE 76

A B C D E F G H I J K L M N O P Q R S T U V W X Y Z

Arrow Words

PUZZLE
77

Stage play	Tearing	Keep away from	Simpson: cartoon character	Small social insect	The day after today	▼	Untimely	▼
▶	▼	▼	▼	▼	Possess			
___ Lendl: former tennis star					Pull		Foreign language (informal)	
Small window on a ship ▶				▼			▼	
Hog ▶				Song for a solo voice ▶				
▶								
Patches of facial hair		Particle that holds quarks together	Charming and elegant	Company symbol ▶				
▶		▼	▼	Was aware of; understood	Came first			
Hens lay these	Third Gospel			▼		Fall behind	Beer	
Chinese monetary unit ▶				Scientific workplace (abbrev) ▶		▼	▼	
Rejuvenate	Generally; in summary ▶							
▶				Command to a horse ▶				

109

After an extensive search, the victim's phone is finally found taped inside the front passenger's side wheel arch. Somehow, the killer has managed to change the phone's lock to a puzzle.

What number will unlock the phone?

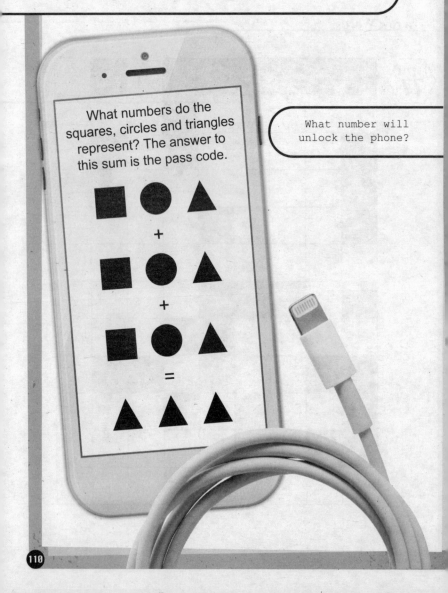

When the team unlocks the phone, Summers notices that the text message icon is flashing. What does the message say?

Sender: Unknown

19 8 5   23 1 19   1   18 21 4 5,
2 9 20 20 5 18   15 12 4   23 15 13 1 14
23 8 15   4 5 19 5 18 22 5 4
5 22 5 18 25 20 8 9 14 7
19 8 5   7 15 20.   9'4   4 15   9 20
1 7 1 9 14   9 6   9   3 15 21 12 4.

Received: 04:36

111

Sara's PUZZLE PAGES

THE BEST-SELLING NEWSPAPER IN GRAVEN END

Pathfinder: Car Parts

PUZZLE
80

A	D	L	S	C	B	U	R	E	T
E	H	I	T	A	R	K	C	A	T
O	T	G	H	N	I	W	F	R	O
O	B	C	S	D	T	S	O	T	R
R	D	R	A	T	L	R	O	Y	R
A	E	E	E	B	E	A	T	S	E
O	N	H	S	G	A	I	S	B	O
B	N	A	A	K	B	R	U	N	N
H	D	B	R	E	B	R	A	E	T
S	A	D	S	E	K	A	H	X	E

AIRBAG	DASHBOARD	ROOF
BONNET	EXHAUST	RACK
BOOT	HANDBRAKE	SEAT BELTS
BRAKES	HEADLIGHTS	TYRES
CARBURETTOR		WINDSCREEN

Codebreaker

PUZZLE
81

	9		1		4		24		20		17	
1	26	9	4	10	17	19	26	21	26	1	19	13
	9		12		17		4		12		4	
9	12	10	15	3	4	10	1		3	4	14	15
			4		18		1		15		8	
18	10	4	11	8	15	1		22	12	13	25	4
	4				1		18				19	
21	11	8	26	22		23	12	10	25	19	4	11
	16		9		1		10		19			
6	4	10	5		9	10	21	15	21	7	21	12
	12		4		12		26		21		8	
12	11	2	4	10	15	8	1	4	22	4	3	15
	1		9		4		4		1		5	

A B C D E F G H I J K L M N O P Q R S T U V W X Y Z

1	2	3	4	5	6	7	8	9	10	11	12	13
S									R			

14	15	16	17	18	19	20	21	22	23	24	25	26
					L							

113

Use this page to record any notes or answers for this crime. This may help you to determine who you think the killer is at the very end.

PUZZLE	ANSWER
57	
58	
61	
64	
65	
68	
69	
72	
75	
78	
79	

Did you notice anything strange about the puzzles in the Graven End newspaper?

Beaten with her own walking stick? Ouch.

Strange killing, though. Merryweather may have been a grumpy old woman, but what harm could she have done to the killer?

Revenge for something? Just for fun?

So far there's not been any DNA evidence from the killer at any of the crime scenes. They're either really good at cleaning up after themselves, or they know what we're looking for. Inside job?

This killing doesn't seem to match that of Jones. Seems to me to be more of a rage killing, more in line with the first crime than the second.

CRIME SCENE FOUR

LOCATION:
WONDERMENT
(a magic shop owned
by The Mysterious
Sydney Blackstone,
aka Joe Fraiser),
High Street

MURDER WEAPON:
Formaldehyde

VICTIM:
Joe Fraiser

The victim had lived in Graven End all of his life. He had a previous conviction for ████████████. As a teenager, the victim studied chemistry at Graven End University, but was expelled after being caught breaking into the administration building in an attempt to change his grades.

Less than an hour before the victim was found face down behind the counter of WONDERMENT by his girlfriend, Sarah Burnham, neighbours had heard the sounds of an argument on the premises. None had reported it to the police, stating that it wasn't uncommon to hear shouting coming from the shop.

Officers find him unconscious at the scene and he later dies in hospital after medics are unable to revive him. A comprehensive toxicology screening completed by the laboratory finds high levels of formaldehyde in his stomach and bloodstream.

Sara's PUZZLE PAGES

THE BEST-SELLING NEWSPAPER IN GRAVEN END

— " —

You are never too old to do another puzzle.

" —

Pathfinder: Herbs and Spices

PUZZLE
82

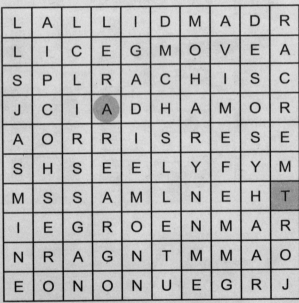

L	A	L	L	I	D	M	A	D	R
L	I	C	E	G	M	O	V	E	A
S	P	L	R	A	C	H	I	S	C
J	C	I	A	D	H	A	M	O	R
A	O	R	R	I	S	R	E	S	E
S	H	S	E	E	L	Y	F	Y	M
M	S	S	A	M	L	N	E	H	T
I	E	G	R	O	E	N	M	A	R
N	R	A	G	N	T	M	M	A	O
E	O	N	O	N	U	E	G	R	J

ALLSPICE	DILL	JASMINE	OREGANO
CARDAMOM	FENNEL	LEMONGRASS	ROSEMARY
CHIVES	GARLIC	MARJORAM	THYME
	HORSERADISH	NUTMEG	

Crossword

PUZZLE 83

Across

1 Device that chops up documents (8)
5 Coalition of countries (4)
8 Move to music (5)
9 Taken as a whole (7)
10 Chats (7)
12 Gloss (7)
14 Most favourable (7)
16 Signs up (7)
18 Suitor (7)
19 Mexican plant fibre (5)
20 Not difficult (4)
21 Breed of dairy cattle (8)

Down

1 Soft drink (US) (4)
2 Pierre-Auguste ___ : French artist (6)
3 Bandages (9)
4 Sufficient (6)
6 Introduction (4-2)
7 Gigantic (8)
11 Luggage items (9)
12 Revere (8)
13 Fastening devices (6)
14 Fish-eating bird of prey (6)
15 Breakfast food (6)
17 Sheet of floating ice (4)

The first thing that Detective McCrawley notices about WONDERMENT is the maze that has been pasted onto the shop window. It looks like there's a message *within* the maze, which is strange. What does it say?

In between showing off his ridiculous card tricks and doing his actual work, Dr. Easton knocks over the shop's phone and this sticky note is found underneath.

99966688
6633333
8666
55566666655
44466
84433
7777233333

Can you work out what it means?

Sara's PUZZLE PAGES

Arrow Words

PUZZLE
86

Currents of air ▼		Close by ▼		Wedding	Person granted a permit ▼		At the present time	Departs
Making law ▶		▼						▼
For each ▶				Queen ___: fairy in Romeo and Juliet	Dove sound			
Injure ▶				▼	Female sheep			
⚑					Military unit		Cut of pork	
Country in Western Asia		Embarrass ▶			▼		▼	Gaming tile
Droop ▶				Peruse ▶				▼
Make a choice	Fill a suitcase	Link a town with another		Short note ▶				
⚑	▼	▼	Greek letter	Tree liquid		Deep hole in the ground	In what way	
Inspires fear and wonder ▶			▼	▼	Hip (anag)	▼		
Quotation ▶								
Summit of a small hill				One and one ▶				

PUZZLE
87

> Winners are not people who never fail, but people who never quit.

Letter-Doku!

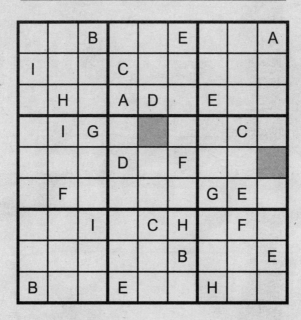

		B			E			A
I			C					
	H		A	D		E		
	I	G					C	
			D		F			
	F					G	E	
		I		C	H		F	
					B			E
B			E			H		

The Crime Scene Techs notice that a piece of
paper has been taped to the front of the safe,
and that the symbols look like the four card
suits. A pack of cards was discovered nearby,
but no immediate connection is found.

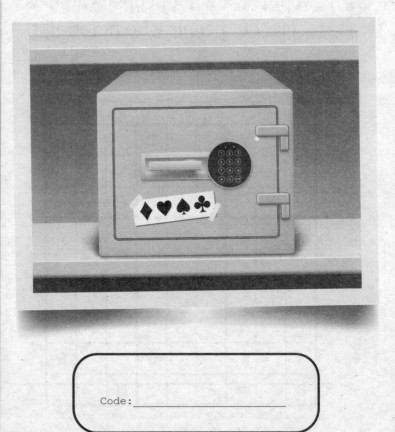

Code: _____

McCrawley spreads the pack of cards out over the shop's sales counter to see if she can find a connection. Can you spot one between the cards, the symbols, and the safe?

Sara's PUZZLE PAGES

Crossword

PUZZLE
89

Across

1 Glassy (8)
5 ___ Khan: British boxer (4)
8 Flexible insulated cables (5)
9 Colloquial speech (7)
10 Imparts knowledge (7)
12 Unit of sound intensity (7)
14 Restrain (7)
16 Pass across or through (7)
18 Far-reaching; thorough (7)
19 Let (5)
20 Fall slowly downwards (4)
21 Sheath for a sword (8)

Down

1 Bad habit (4)
2 Material used for surfacing roads (6)
3 Groups of performers (9)
4 Uncover (6)
6 Scanty (6)
7 Type of resistor (8)
11 Boxing film with Brad Pitt (5,4)
12 Upsets; agitates (8)
13 Make unhappy (6)
14 Sloping (of a typeface) (6)
15 Yellow fruit (6)
17 Peruse (4)

You've got this. Never doubt yourself.

Kriss Kross

3 letters
Boa
Coy
Ell
Ski
Ton
Tub

4 letters
Bran
Club
Ebbs
Else
Pier
Pint
Posh
Rued

6 letters
Anoint
Earths
Tiling
Tutors

7 letters
Anodyne
Nibbled

8 letters
Assesses
Bagpiper
Confetti
Elevator
Escapist
Initiate
Malaysia
Subtract
Thanking
Wretched

9 letters
Egotistic
Embattled

Inside the safe is a ledger detailing WONDERMENT'S transactions. Dusting reveals a number of different partial fingerprints. Can you match them to the fingerprints that are on file, or that we've seen so far throughout the case?

Stock #	Cost £	Date	Name
31235	47.02	3rd	Herbert Nelson
56464	16.12		Ida McDonald
56588	5.46	4th	Dilbert Warner
315568	11.09		Chris Penn
64544	0.49		Stanley Connely
56276	7.99		Ezra Catt
62752	9.50		Michael Harker
76727	6.40		Delia King
76272	4.46	5th	Leo Santana
36842	9.16		Daniel Penner
75756	33.66		Jeremiah Bulb
121135	5.69	6th	Steven Mantle
35158	7.44		Sarah Jones
41252	4.45	7th	Tommy O'Shea
78966	8.64		Barbara Craton
31535	4.45		Chad McDuckett
12152	7.37		Jack Cather
22256	57.53		Henry Weeks
45345	7.30	8th	Walt Whitty
35158	10.40		
76727	4.04		
31556	4.54		
45756	.6.35		
64544	3.85		
36842	1.25		
75275			

Stock #	Cost £	
31235	3.73	
35158	14.72	
64544	7.43	
75275	17.29	
74535	7.38	
63875	6.66	
89393	45.52	
10455	6.37	
73753	19.50	
12347	0.49	
76272	33.66	R
48651	9.66	
76375	13.56	
45354	6.78	
52572	4.35	
45757	6.87	
64544	10.59	
33387	19.21	
91351	0.49	

07.2020 1711

Joe Fraiser
Victim

Artie Fraiser
Victim's nephew
Sometimes helps out at
the shop

Darren Miller
Accountant
Looks over the books on
a monthly basis

Sarah Burnham
Victim's girlfriend
Was in the shop the
evening of the murder

Toby Underwood
Customer (Child)
A frequent visitor, often
visiting to watch the
victim perform tricks

Jeremiah Bull
Customer
Witnessed having an
argument with the victim
less than half an hour
before the murder

Sara's PUZZLE PAGES

THE BEST-SELLING NEWSPAPER IN GRAVEN END

PUZZLE
92

A - Z

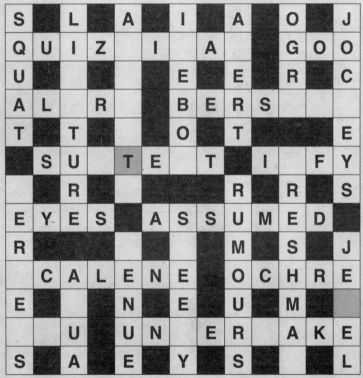

A B C D E F G H I J K L M N O P Q R S T U V W X Y Z

Pathfinder: Family

PUZZLE 93

AUNT
BROTHER
CLAN
COUSIN
DESCENDANTS
FAMILY TREE
GRANDMOTHER
HERITAGE
HUSBAND
IN-LAW
NIECE
PARTNER
SPOUSE
UNCLE
WIFE

O	U	A	N	P	A	R	T	N	E
P	S	L	H	T	O	R	B	C	R
S	E	C	E	G	R	A	T	O	U
E	E	N	R	D	N	N	N	U	S
T	R	I	S	B	A	D	M	A	I
Y	C	E	U	H	E	T	O	W	N
L	E	C	L	E	G	H	E	A	I
I	U	N	E	H	A	W	R	L	N
M	S	T	R	I	T	I	F	E	D
A	F	N	A	D	N	E	C	S	E

> All will make sense soon enough.
> Just keep going.

Inside the back of the ledger is an old receipt for the installation of a second safe – a floor safe in the basement. Upon conducting a search of the basement, an officer finds the following note taped to a shelf.

Oh dear. All these paving stones look the same and you can't dig up the whole basement...

	51		58			62			
49					80				66
	54	56			93	99		96	68
40	47		77			100	98		
	41			◯		91			
35					84		87		
						73	72	26	
			31		29				
		16	17	18		20	21	1	3
12					7				

Solve the Journeys puzzle to find the correct paving stone to reveal the safe.

Careful removal of the paving stone reveals a digital combination safe sunk into the floor, and a piece of paper with familiar writing.

| 3 | 5 | 4 | 8 | *One digit is right but it is in the wrong place* |

| 4 | 6 | 7 | 1 | *Two digits are correct but only one is in the correct place* |

| 3 | 7 | 8 | 1 | *Two digits are correct but both are in the wrong place* |

| 8 | 3 | 9 | 7 | *One digit is wrong. The others are correct but in the wrong places* |

| 5 | 2 | 1 | 4 | *All digits are wrong* |

| 2 | 9 | 3 | 4 | *One digit is right but it is in the wrong place* |

| 5 | 1 | 3 | 6 | *One digit is both right and in the correct place* |

Code: _____

Sara's PUZZLE PAGES

Codebreaker

PUZZLE
96

19	8	4	2	10	■	17	25	5	24	4	2	10
5	■	25	■	2	■	5	■	■	5	■	15	■
2	■	13	■	3	■	25	■	21	25	1	13	26
23	25	12	11	13	16	18	9	■	6	■	4	■
16	■	10	■	12	■	18	■	20	2	18	26	18
18	26	5	16	14	22	2	12	■	12	■	■	2
16	■	7	■	26	■	■	■	25	■	18	■	19
8	■	■	14	■	8	19	2	5	2	26	26	25
12	16	21	9	26	■	8	■	26	■	8	■	5
■	5	■	25	■	2	26	9	16	8	19	16	25
1	8	5	19	9	■	2	■	14	■	19	■	26
■	12	■	2	■	■	12	■	4	■	2	■	2
14	7	14	4	16	18	26	■	2	5	5	2	10

A B C D E F G H I J K L M N O P Q R S T U V W X Y Z

1	2	3	4	5	6	7	8	9	10	11	12	13
		F							D			

14	15	16	17	18	19	20	21	22	23	24	25	26
	X											

Word Search: Pop Groups

PUZZLE 97

O	M	Q	I	O	M	S	E	L	G	N	A	B	S	D
A	X	K	U	V	Z	A	I	P	U	Q	L	N	U	B
S	Z	J	G	E	E	R	B	X	X	S	L	B	S	R
I	Y	W	M	Y	E	N	O	B	J	L	S	P	L	R
S	V	A	T	A	S	N	I	Y	A	T	A	E	R	F
D	R	O	L	I	D	U	U	J	A	N	I	T	I	Y
F	K	A	J	P	E	N	T	R	D	F	N	S	G	A
S	R	S	U	N	D	E	E	A	R	L	T	H	E	S
I	H	O	A	T	O	L	U	S	X	A	S	O	C	S
S	B	E	A	C	H	B	O	Y	S	O	S	P	I	C
E	Z	T	E	X	A	S	X	C	O	M	C	B	P	L
N	G	I	R	L	S	A	L	O	U	D	F	O	S	U
E	F	I	L	T	S	E	W	E	N	O	Z	Y	O	B
G	S	E	U	R	Y	T	H	M	I	C	S	S	Y	X
P	T	Y	G	Y	O	L	J	E	A	O	O	Y	U	S

ABBA	COLDPLAY	PET SHOP BOYS
ALL SAINTS	DUBSTAR	QUEEN
BANGLES	EURYTHMICS	S CLUB
BEACH BOYS	GENESIS	SPANDAU BALLET
BON JOVI	GIRLS ALOUD	SPICE GIRLS
BONEY M	MADNESS	TEXAS
BOYZONE	OASIS	WESTLIFE

Transcript of conversation between Detective Sergeant
Katie McCrawley and Detective Constable Alex Summers,
conducted via text message.

Summers: its full of champagne

McCrawley: What?

Summers: the safe. Theres 20 bottles of champagne
             in it

McCrawley: is it cheap, One-Stop-Pop-And-Shop stuff?

Summers: Dont think so. never heard of some of it

McCrawley: right. anything else?

Summers: yep. word search. 21 different champagne
             names on it.

McCrawley: do they match the bottles in the safe?

Summers: Yep, looks like it.

McCrawley: but there r only 20 bottles in the safe?

Summers: oh, so 1 is missing. clever!

McCrawley: 1 of us has to be...

[END OF TRANSCRIPT]

136

```
R P W K S S M L Y A H A S R X
E G O N E V E D M E L V X T X
I B Y L A N S O N A M L T K R
R B O T A T S R Y T S S E I R
R P R G F P I A M M U M S P V
E N E T T O M A L E D R S A L
P A L J T M R W V O R C O D L
T L L E R M E B T J N C G B U
N G A E U E G L G H E J I I T
E R V P I R N E C A T T I E R
R K U E N Y I Z U M T G Y R R
U I D R A L L I A P O N U R B
A B P Q R V L O H G G S K R E
L D E U T Z O B T Y A R I C K
O O A A U T B U R K A R X K A
```

AYALA	DEUTZ	LAURENT-PERRIER
BOIZEL	DUVAL-LEROY	MERCIER
BOLLINGER	GOSSET	MUMM
BRUNO PAILLARD	HENRIOT	POL ROGER
CATTIER	JEEPER	POMMERY
DE VENOGE	KRUG	RUINART
DELAMOTTE	LANSON	SALON

Use the word search to work out which of
the champagne bottles is missing.

137

Sara's PUZZLE PAGES

Kriss Kross

PUZZLE 99

3 letters
Coo
Gas
Ivy
Pop
Tic
Tor

5 letters
Audio
Croft
Dwell
Emery
Flirt
Least
Needy
Occur
Sedan
Tubes

7 letters
Abyssal
Diorama
Elegant
Flotsam
Gorilla
Oxidise
Pimples
Satisfy

8 letters
Glorious
Luscious
Militant
Plethora
Rightful
Tricycle

9 letters
Flowerpot
Yachtsman

13 letters
Abbreviations
Inexperienced

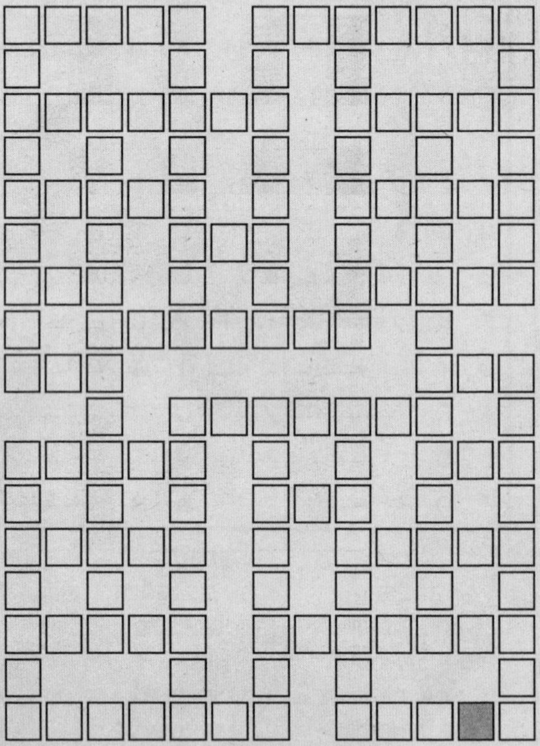

Crossword

PUZZLE
100

Across

1 One image within another (5)
4 Getting bigger (7)
7 Body of burning gas (5)
8 Create an account deficit (8)
9 Leashes (5)
11 ___ hour: the latest possible moment (8)
15 Higher in rank (8)
17 Make law (5)
19 Harmful (8)
20 Garment worn in the kitchen (5)
21 James Joyce novel (7)
22 The Norwegian language (5)

Down

1 Impertinence (9)
2 Plotter (7)
3 Walks laboriously (7)
4 Racing vehicle (2-4)
5 Drooped (6)
6 Titled (5)
10 One deputising for another (9)
12 Edible jelly (7)
13 Separator (7)
14 ___ the board: applying to all (6)
16 Seventh planet (6)
18 Country in the Himalayas (5)

Underneath the bottles in the safe is a tiny little notebook, filled with code. It looks like it's a list of who bought which bottles, but it needs decoding.

April
  6th   4 23   12 1 14 19 15 13

May
  1st   13 18   12 1 21 18 5 14 20-16 5 18 18 9 5 18
  9th   19 3   2 15 12 12 9 14 7 5 18
  10th   3 13   11 18 21 7

June
  1st   5 3   3 1 20 20 9 5 18
  3rd   8 14   2 15 12 12 9 14 7 5 18
  5th   12 19   16 15 12   18 15 7 5 18 19
  7th   2 3   13 21 14 14

Once you've decoded it, look at the initials. Do any of them look familiar to you?

D	K	K	L	R	E	E	N	A	C	C	U	B	Q	T
D	R	E	K	A	E	R	B	E	S	U	O	H	P	N
D	E	I	R	I	R	S	D	F	J	N	U	R	T	I
E	K	X	N	B	D	C	S	G	U	B	S	E	R	S
W	C	W	T	K	C	N	E	A	V	T	X	L	E	S
P	A	A	S	O	D	R	A	N	P	P	L	G	G	A
I	R	R	T	H	R	R	A	P	I	S	T	N	G	S
C	C	E	C	B	O	T	I	W	P	S	E	A	E	S
K	E	G	D	R	U	P	I	V	L	E	T	R	L	A
P	F	G	O	I	I	R	L	O	E	E	R	T	T	E
O	A	U	I	G	R	M	G	I	N	R	R	S	O	P
C	S	M	T	A	D	Y	I	L	F	I	R	M	O	Y
K	A	Z	V	N	T	G	O	N	A	T	S	H	B	O
E	S	L	K	D	A	F	V	J	A	R	E	T	G	O
T	S	B	L	A	C	K	M	A	I	L	E	R	X	R

ASSASSIN	EXTORTIONIST	MUGGER
BLACKMAILER	FORGER	PICKPOCKET
BOOTLEGGER	HOUSEBREAKER	SAFE-CRACKER
BRIGAND	JOYRIDER	SHOPLIFTER
BUCCANEER	KERB-CRAWLER	STRANGLER
CAT-BURGLAR	KIDNAPPER	TRESPASSER
DRINK-DRIVER	LARCENIST	WAR CRIMINAL

The Lab finds this word search pasted onto one of the bottles. Can you work out if it's a clue left behind by the killer?

Sara's PUZZLE PAGES

THE BEST-SELLING NEWSPAPER IN GRAVEN END

If you think about it, everything is a puzzle.

PUZZLE 103

Word Search: 'Ace' Words

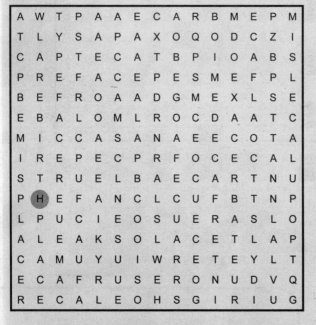

A	W	T	P	A	A	E	C	A	R	B	M	E	P	M
T	L	Y	S	A	P	A	X	O	Q	O	D	C	Z	I
C	A	P	T	E	C	A	T	B	P	I	O	A	B	S
P	R	E	F	A	C	E	P	E	S	M	E	F	P	L
B	E	F	R	O	A	A	D	G	M	E	X	L	S	E
E	B	A	L	O	M	L	R	O	C	D	A	A	T	C
M	I	C	C	A	S	A	N	A	E	E	C	O	T	A
I	R	E	P	E	C	P	R	F	O	C	E	C	A	L
S	T	R	U	E	L	B	A	E	C	A	R	T	N	U
P	H	E	F	A	N	C	L	C	U	F	B	T	N	P
L	P	U	C	I	E	O	S	U	E	R	A	S	L	O
A	L	E	A	K	S	O	L	A	C	E	T	L	A	P
C	A	M	U	Y	U	I	W	R	E	T	E	Y	L	T
E	C	A	F	R	U	S	E	R	O	N	U	D	V	Q
R	E	C	A	L	E	O	H	S	G	I	R	I	U	G

AEROSPACE
BIRTHPLACE
COALFACE
COMMONPLACE
DEFACE
DISGRACEFUL
EMBRACE
EXACERBATE
INTERFACE
MAINBRACE
MISPLACE
PACED
PEACE
POPULACE
PREFACE
RESURFACE
SHOELACE
SOLACE
TACET
TYPEFACE
UNTRACEABLE

Codebreaker

PUZZLE 104

23	21	26	3	10	4	15	6		26	4	15	14
2		19		12		10		8		24		19
1	4	20	5	2		11		10	26	3	4	11
1		15		8		7		15		19		10
			5	4	26	4	26	20	4	5	4	8
6		5		18		5		4		6		2
16	19	4	17	21	11		15	11	4	4	3	22
10		6		2		4		10		8		15
15	6	5	21	13	6	21	5	4	8			
6		4		10		5		7		10		6
10	26	2	25	4		4		10	12	17	4	5
12		6		15		9		12		17		21
25	21	15	6		25	2	5	25	19	22	11	4

A B C D E F G H I J K L M N O P Q R S T U V W X Y Z

1	2	3	4	5	6	7	8	9	10	11	12	13
						V						C

14	15	16	17	18	19	20	21	22	23	24	25	26
												M

...ntations – one before bottling, and one in the bottle be... is drunk. The second fermentation produces the car-...ioxide and ethanol that are vital for the finished product.

Chemical Analysis of Champagne

The average 0.75 litre bottle of champagne contains 7.5 grams of dissolved carbon dioxide. When the bottle is opened, it releases approximately 5 litres of carbon dioxide gas before becoming completely flat. A single champagne flute, assuming a volume of 0.1 litres, contains approximately 20 million bubbles.

The Graven End Lab runs a carbon dioxide analysis on the 20 bottles of champagne. Do any of them match the control sample?

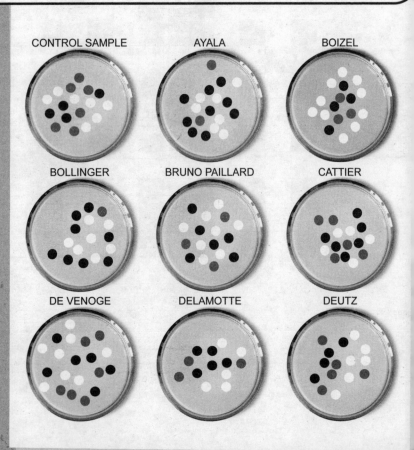

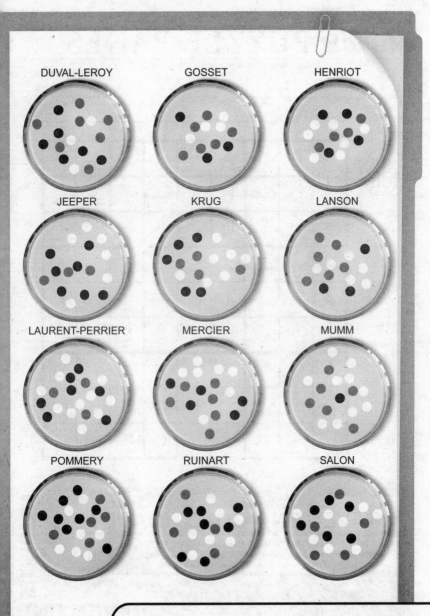

DUVAL-LEROY   GOSSET   HENRIOT

JEEPER   KRUG   LANSON

LAURENT-PERRIER   MERCIER   MUMM

POMMERY   RUINART   SALON

What can you conclude from this experiment?

145

Sara's PUZZLE PAGES

Letter-Doku!

PUZZLE 106

	C		A			I		
	G		H	I			A	
F			C					
		D						F
A			I		F			H
I					E			
					B			D
	F			H	I		B	
		G			C		F	

Crossword

PUZZLE
107

Across

1 Walks up and down (5)
4 E.g. from Ethiopia (7)
7 Appeal (5)
8 Suspenseful adventure story (8)
9 Craftily (5)
11 Official list of names (8)
15 Popular lunch food (8)
17 Particle that holds quarks together (5)
19 Wheeled supermarket vehicles (8)
20 Embed; type of filling (5)
21 Segmented worm (7)
22 MacArthur: sailor (5)

Down

1 Vain posing (9)
2 Bravery (7)
3 Smart and fashionable (7)
4 Assent or agree to (6)
5 Breathe in (6)
6 Pertaining to the ear (5)
10 Sailor of a light vessel (9)
12 Flatter (7)
13 Given generously (7)
14 Place where something is set (6)
16 Overseas (6)
18 Cloth woven from flax (5)

147

In their haste to solve the case, one of the officers takes the champagne bottles out of the safe before the Crime Scene Techs could photograph them. He only remembers the location of 3 bottles. Can you recreate the positions of all the bottles? Some could go in more than one location, which is fine as the Techs just need an approximate layout.

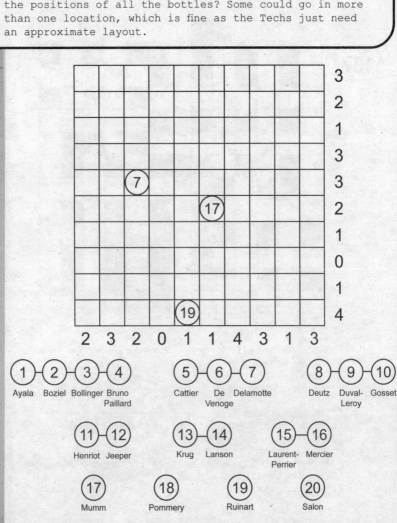

The grid has the following row totals (top to bottom): 3, 2, 1, 3, 3, 2, 1, 0, 1, 4. Inside the grid: a 7 is placed, a 17 is placed, and a 19 is placed. The column totals (left to right) are: 2, 3, 2, 0, 1, 1, 4, 3, 1, 3.

(1)—(2)—(3)—(4)
Ayala Boziel Bollinger Bruno Paillard

(5)—(6)—(7)
Cattier De Venoge Delamotte

(8)—(9)—(10)
Deutz Duval-Leroy Gosset

(11)—(12)
Henriot Jeeper

(13)—(14)
Krug Lanson

(15)—(16)
Laurent-Perrier Mercier

(17)
Mumm

(18)
Pommery

(19)
Ruinart

(20)
Salon

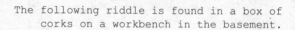

The following riddle is found in a box of corks on a workbench in the basement.

A person was locked in a room. In it were two doors, a table and chair, and a hole in the ceiling 15cm wide. Behind the first door was a hungry lion. Behind the second door was a glass tunnel that magnified the sun, creating a temperature so high that it would scorch you if you opened the door. The person escaped.

How?

After solving the riddle, McCrawley looks up. Sure enough, she can see a small hole in the ceiling, next to the light fixture. A tiny camera is found, looking directly down at the work table. While initially the team are excited to find out the identity of the killer, they soon realise that the cheap, rubbish camera takes cheap, rubbish video. Only two stills are decent enough to see anything.

It looks like the items on the desk have changed. Can you find the **six** differences between the two photos?

Use this page to record all your answers for this crime. This may help you to determine who you think the killer is at the very end.

PUZZLE	ANSWER
84	
85	
88	
91	
94	
95	
98	
101	
102	
105	
108	
109	
110	

Did you notice anything strange about the puzzles in the Graven End newspaper?

So, Frasier was a forger. Admittedly, I never saw that one coming, but there was always something... off about him. Incredibly intelligent, but just not sure how to use it? However, from what Easton says, formaldehyde poisoning is a horrible way to go. To slip it in the champagne is a little bit of genius.

I notice that the name Leo Santana keeps popping up, first in Jones' murder and then in Frasier's. I don't know of anyone by that name. The university has records, but they're sealed, and Turner doesn't think "my gut feeling" warrants a judge ordering them unsealed. All the records I can find — bank, driving licence, etc — just end after the 70s. Like he died?

Probably just coincidence. You're over thinking this, McCrawley.

CRIME SCENE FIVE

CONFIDENTIAL

LOCATION:
The Egyptian wing of the Graven End Historical Society Museum

MURDER WEAPON:
A bronze amulet (lodged in his esophagus)

ELEMENTS OF THE FILE HAVE BEEN REDACTED DUE TO THE HIGHLY CONFIDENTIAL NATURE OF THE CASE. THE FILE AND CONTENTS ARE THE PROPERTY OF THE GRAVEN END POLICE DEPARTMENT. REMOVAL FROM THE BUILDING WILL RESULT IN IMMEDIATE ARREST.

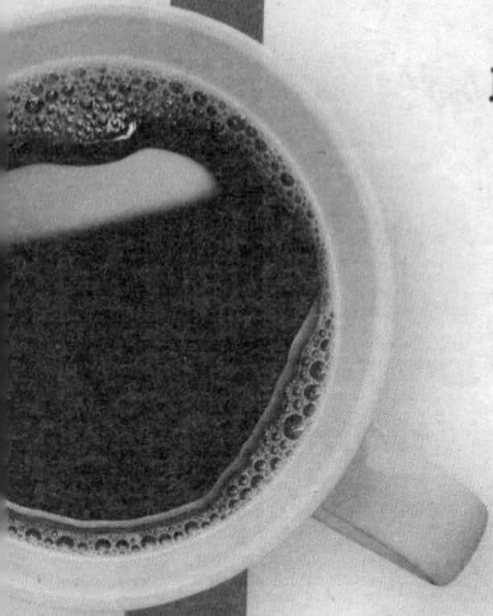

VICTIM: Dr. Anthony Masterson

Before the museum, the victim worked in the medical department at Graven End University, where he taught the history of medicine. His appointment as Head Curator at the museum twenty years ago was welcomed by most, but opposed by some who felt he was too critical of the authenticity of some of the museum's artefacts.

He was often seen arguing with the museum's owner, Matthew Jessup, over large sums paid for unauthenticated items, and how neither the victim nor Jessup were able to ███████████ ████████████████████████ ███████████.

The morning before a special press event was due to be held, unveiling a new treasure, the victim was found dead inside the museum. A small, precious amulet, taken from the museum's bronze display, was found lodged in his throat.

Sara's PUZZLE PAGES

Crossword

PUZZLE
111

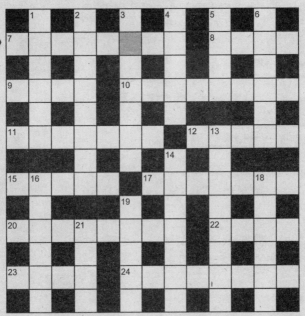

Across

7. Unstrap (8)
8. Use these to row a boat (4)
9. Burkina ___ : African country (4)
10. Pleasantness (8)
11. Sticks to (7)
12. Smash into another vehicle (5)
15. Crunch; wear down (5)
17. Narrow fissure (7)
20. Cocktail (8)
22. Central (4)
23. Flaring star (4)
24. Prodigal (8)

Down

1. Ahead (6)
2. E.g. from Italy or Spain (8)
3. Thick-___ : insensitive to criticism (7)
4. Barrier (5)
5. Sprinkled with seed (4)
6. Comes up (6)
13. Renovated (8)
14. Walk aimlessly (7)
16. Explanation (6)
18. Exclusive circle of people (6)
19. Opinions (5)
21. Wharf (4)

Arrow Words

PUZZLE
112

Tree		Manages		Animal carapaces	Entrance		Machine; automaton	Uttered
Learned people								
				Far away from home	First on the list			
Protective foot covering	Inactive pill							
Squander	Creature with pointed ears				Frying pan			
Gems	Fencing sword	Equipped	Recycle		Grain storage chambers		Express; complete	
						Headland		Dispatched
Foretells								
Flightless bird				Tardy				
				Unwrap a gift				
Pollinating insects	Sweet course							

This word search has been left on the steps of the police station. The officer on duty puts it on Detective McCrawley's desk, but doesn't try to solve it. Can you?

```
Q O T R O U K U Z S H E O A A
V Y K S W Q U A S C I L E R P
I T S S T E N I B A C M R R U
S I T T S T L L E C H U S C M
I R A R I E E Y R O T S I H O
T U T Q N B W D L S P E E W H
O C U C K A I H C T H U I L C
R E E R G S S H C U X M P U D
S S S P P U L G X M K I R A Q
S L T L O P I O F E R B B T A
Y K A H T H S D U S O E N A Q
T Y C B T Y S A E R W J A Y J
S X T P E N O A S S T E Z L Y
U S J Z R L F D E R R A P K I
D S T I Y S S R E T A S Q Z N
```

ANTIQUES	EXHIBITS	QUIET
ARTWORK	FOSSILS	RELICS
CABINETS	GUIDES	SECURITY
COSTUMES	HISTORY	SILENCE
CURATOR	LABELS	STATUES
DISPLAYS	MUSEUM	TEASHOP
DUSTY	POTTERY	VISITORS

Transcript of conversation between Detective Sergeant Katie McCrawley and Detective Constable Alex Summers, conducted via text message.

McCrawley: Theres another 1

Summers: seriously?

McCrawley: Yea. Looks like the curator @ GE museum

Summers: What r they playing @? I havent even eaten breakfast yet

McCrawley: No idea

McCrawley: Dont think he cares about ur brkfast, tho

McCrawley: heading over in 10

Summers: right. Meet u there in 30?

McCrawley: oh by all means take ur time with brkfast. its only a murder. nothing special

Summers: bUT theyre pancakes

McCrawley: ...

[END OF TRANSCRIPT]

Sara's PUZZLE PAGES

THE BEST-SELLING NEWSPAPER IN GRAVEN END

Codebreaker

PUZZLE
114

22	24	10	4	6		22	17	7	13	7	13	18
16		13		16		16			16		4	
15		14		12		6		24	21	16	3	4
4	6	5	24	12	7	6	22		21		1	
6		10		14		20		8	20	14	4	6
5	11	4	3	3	7	4	6		4			26
4		2		22				6		25		16
13			7		24	20	20	4	20	16	7	24
22	11	7	13	18		14		24		25		17
	24		2		25	14	19	6	22	7	5	10
12	7	23	7	4		6		14		22		7
	3		18			4		13		6		13
9	19	18	14	13	4	6		6	17	16	13	18

A B C D E F G H I J K L M N O P Q R S T U V W X Y Z

1	2	3	4	5	6	7	8	9	10	11	12	13
	D						F					

14	15	16	17	18	19	20	21	22	23	24	25	26
								T				

160

Crossword

PUZZLE
115

Across

1 Small restaurant (4)
3 Unusual (8)
9 In a nimble manner (7)
10 Religious doctrine (5)
11 Trite (anag) (5)
12 Seven-a-side game (7)
13 Strong (6)
15 Restore honour (6)
17 Tidies (7)
18 Alcoholic beverage (5)
20 Dwelling (5)
21 Break between words (in verse) (7)
22 Buffed (8)
23 Nuisance plant (4)

Down

1 Artisanship (13)
2 Force upon (5)
4 Purchasing (6)
5 Fully extended (12)
6 Artificial (3-4)
7 The ___ / ___ : Fairy tale by Hans Christian Andersen (6,7)
8 Notwithstanding (12)
14 Not sudden (7)
16 Soul; spirit (6)
19 Extinguish (a fire) (5)

Less than ten minutes after the puzzle has been solved, officers arrive at the museum. This note is found taped above the electronic keypad on the locked door of the staff entrance.

Officers. I have hidden three puzzles in this alleyway.
Complete all three to receive the code to this door.
Don't take too long, though...

2	◯				7	3	4	
8	4					9		2
	1		4	8				7
				3			8	6
			8		5			
3	8			6		◯		
4				2	6		7	
1		2					5	4
	3	8	5					1

The second puzzle is found tucked underneath a
bucket in the corner of the alley.

Number Two

		7		4			◯	8
	1	4	3					
6	2		1					9
		6	8					
4		◯		1				5
					4	2		
1					7		5	6
					3	9	7	
7			5	9		3		

Hurry up....

The final sudoku is found by Summers, tucked into the street sign.

Last one. Have you worked it out yet?

		3						5
8				5	2		6	
◯						2	7	
4				1	7	5		2
5		2	8	6				3
	4	8			◯			
	2		4	7				8
1						6		

Full Code: _____

VE

As McCrawley enters the staff room, she notices an officer staring at the letterboard on the wall. When asked, the officer replies that "there are missing letters. I just can't work out which ones".

CAN WE REMEMBER O R ATES, PLE SE? DONT
LET YOU SELF B CAUGH UT. HILDREN
ALW YS OVE TO SEE US FUMB E.
RE EMB R AARON?

STONE GE	2.5 MI LION-3000 BCE
BRONZE AGE	3000-1300 BCE
RON GE	1300-600 BCE
PERSIAN EMPI E	550 BCE-330 BCE
NCIENT REECE	600 BCE-600 D
ANC ENT ROME	753 BCE-476 AD
MIDDLE AGES	476 AD-1450 AD
BYZANTINE EMPIRE	285 AD-1453 AD
EUROPEAN RE AISSANCE	1450 AD-1600 AD

Sara's PUZZLE PAGES

THE BEST-SELLING NEWSPAPER IN GRAVEN END

A - Z

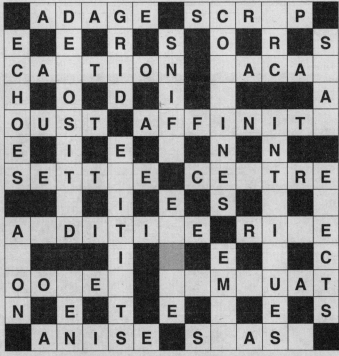

PUZZLE 120

	A	D	A	G	E		S	C	R		P	
E		E		R	S		O		R			S
C	A		T	I	O	N		A	C	A		
H		O		D		I						A
O	U	S	T		A	F	F	I	N	I	T	
E		I		E			N			N		
S	E	T	T		E		C	E		T	R	E
				I		E	S					
A		D	I	T	I	E		E		R	I	E
				I				E				C
O	O		E					M		U	A	T
N		E		T		E				E		S
	A	N	I	S	E		S		A	S		

A B C D E F G H I J K L M N O P Q R S T U V W X Y Z

166

Kriss Kross

PUZZLE 121

3 letters	7 letters
Arc	Ecuador
Elm	Elastin
Icy	Erratum
Nod	Octagon
	Polemic
4 letters	Topiary
Ajar	
Eels	**8 letters**
Epic	Anecdote
Muck	Employed
Ogre	Leapfrog
Race	Nickname

5 letters	9 letters
Gecko	Contralto
Olden	Margarine
Stern	Misdirect
Stomp	Objecting

6 letters	13 letters
Bounce	Communication
Casing	
Except	
Gallic	
Pigsty	
Tidied	

PUZZLE
122

The Crime Scene Techs find nothing in the staff room, but they do report that all the lockers are empty, except one. They are unable to look inside the locker, as it is locked with a combination padlock. There is no code nearby, but there is another puzzle taped to the back of the staff room door.

If you want to look in the locker, you're going to have to work out the combination first...

There are 10 lockers and 10 members of staff. All lockers are closed. As the staff enter, the first employee (E1), opens every locker. Then the second employee (E2) begins with the second locker, L2, and closes every other locker. Employee E3 begins with the third locker and changes every third locker (closes it if it was open and opens it if it was closed). Employee (E4) starts at locker L4 and changes every fourth locker. Employee E5 starts with locker L5 and changes every fifth locker, and so on, until employee 10 changes locker 10.

After all the employees have passed through the locker room and changed the lockers, which lockers are open?

Open = ✓

Closed = ✗

LOCKERS

EMPLOYEES

	1	2	3	4	5	6	7	8	9	10
1										
2										
3										
4										
5										
6										
7										
8										
9										
10										

Code: _____

Sara's PUZZLE PAGES

Pathfinder: Capital Cities

PUZZLE 123

ADDIS ABABA
AMSTERDAM
BAGHDAD
BANGKOK
BRIDGETOWN
DUBLIN
HAMILTON
KUALA LUMPUR
LA PAZ
LAGOS
LONDON
NAIROBI
ULAN BATOR

H	G	I	D	D	A	R	B	R	O
D	A	S	A	B	N	I	D	A	T
A	B	L	B	A	W	E	G	B	N
D	N	I	U	B	O	T	U	L	A
L	N	G	D	A	R	O	N	O	T
A	A	K	N	A	I	B	I	L	L
G	B	O	K	M	A	A	P	A	I
O	N	N	O	L	D	Z	H	A	M
S	O	D	A	L	R	E	T	S	M
K	U	A	L	U	M	P	U	R	A

> The world is a puzzle.
> One we'll never make sense of.

Letter-Doku!

PUZZLE 124

B								D
	G	E					I	
	A				E		G	
			D	C			A	
		D	E		A	B		
	B			I	F			
		G		B			D	
		C				E	G	
E								H

The locker contains three bars of melted chocolate (whole nut), four pens (ink dried up), and a maze. Can you work your way through it and find out which area it's leading us to?

DRUID
DISPLAY

MEXICAN
MONUMENTS

YOU ARE
HERE

GRAVEN END
GALLERY

172

EGYPTIAN
EXHIBIT

CHINESE
CORNER

Sara's PUZZLE PAGES

THE BEST-SELLING NEWSPAPER IN GRAVEN END

Word Search: Roller-Coaster Types

PUZZLE
126

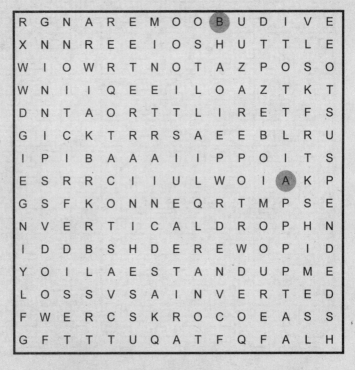

R	G	N	A	R	E	M	O	O	B	U	D	I	V	E
X	N	N	R	E	E	I	O	S	H	U	T	T	L	E
W	I	O	W	R	T	N	O	T	A	Z	P	O	S	O
W	N	I	I	Q	E	E	I	L	O	A	Z	T	K	T
D	N	T	A	O	R	T	T	L	I	R	E	T	F	S
G	I	C	K	T	R	R	S	A	E	E	B	L	R	U
I	P	I	B	A	A	A	I	I	P	P	O	I	T	S
E	S	R	R	C	I	I	U	L	W	O	I	A	K	P
G	S	F	K	O	N	N	E	Q	R	T	M	P	S	E
N	V	E	R	T	I	C	A	L	D	R	O	P	H	N
I	D	D	B	S	H	D	E	R	E	W	O	P	I	D
Y	O	I	L	A	E	S	T	A	N	D	U	P	M	E
L	O	S	S	V	S	A	I	N	V	E	R	T	E	D
F	W	E	R	C	S	K	R	O	C	O	E	A	S	S
G	F	T	T	U	Q	A	T	F	Q	F	A	L	H

BOOMERANG	MINE TRAIN	STAND-UP
CORKSCREW	MOTORBIKE	STEEPLECHASE
DIVE	PIPELINE	SUSPENDED
DUAL-TRACKED	POWERED	TERRAIN
FLOORLESS	SHUTTLE	TWISTER
FLYING	SIDE FRICTION	VERTICAL DROP
INVERTED	SPINNING	WING

Letter-Doku!

PUZZLE 127

G							E	C
		B	I				D	
	F		D		C			
			E				G	H
F								A
C	G				A			
			B		G		C	
	H				D	G		
A	I							D

— ❝ —

Amazing puzzles are coming your way.
Just keep going.

— ❞ —

175

When McCrawley and Summers arrive at the Egyptian
area of the museum, they notice that a piece of
paper has been laid on the information desk.

Where oh where is your next clue?

	22			19			11		9
		27	54			16	14		
				59	58				
		61	63	64			1	6	5
	51								4
			99	100			72	68	
32				98	92	89	76		
						88	85		
	37		44	47					◯
35		38	39				82	80	

When the police officers find the correct location, they come face-to-face with a row of six ancient mummies. The lead curator of the Egyptian exhibits is horrified to find out that one of the mummies has a note stapled to its delicate wrappings.

Oh dear. These mummies are out of order. What terrible person could commit such a crime? Can you work out which one actually goes where? If you do, I promise there's a clue in it for you...

Front Row   ① ② ③

Back Row   ④ ⑤ ⑥

Mummy A: This one is not next to, in front of, or behind Mummy C

Mummy B: This one is not in the front row

Mummy C: Don't put this one on the left or the right

Mummy D: This one shouldn't be put in the back row, or on the left

Mummy E: This mummy is on the right

Mummy F: This one is not on the front, or on the left

So, which mummy goes where? Tick tock, Detective...

Sara's PUZZLE PAGES

Crossword

PUZZLE
130

Across

7 ___ Q: musical (6)
8 Fast (6)
10 Light fabric often made of silk (7)
11 Henrik ___ : Norwegian dramatist (5)
12 Flat and smooth (4)
13 Growing thickly (of a beard) (5)
17 ___ Bellamy: Welsh footballer (5)
18 Adult male singing voice (4)
22 Female fox (5)
23 Not tidy (7)
24 Underground store (6)
25 Matures (of fruit) (6)

Down

1 Large farms (7)
2 Stopped working (7)
3 Deep chasms (5)
4 Standing erect (7)
5 Make fun of someone (5)
6 Doglike mammal (5)
9 Harmful (9)
14 Decorative altar cloth (7)
15 Locked down (7)
16 Boorish (7)
19 Kick out (5)
20 Expel from a country (5)
21 Hank of wool (5)

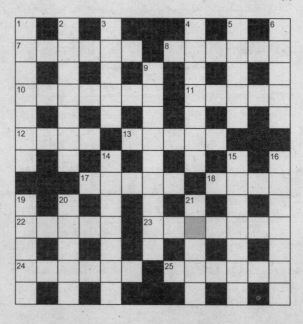

PUZZLE 131

Soon you'll find your answer and all will make sense.

Pathfinder: Yummy Sandwich Fillings

E	G	A	O	Y	A	M	B	Y	T
E	U	S	N	N	N	N	A	E	U
G	A	O	M	A	E	O	C	K	R
G	S	N	L	I	K	C	I	H	C
S	T	C	A	S	A	C	R	A	M
A	O	A	S	E	N	B	A	P	S
L	R	R	P	T	U	C	N	E	S
A	D	I	M	Y	R	E	I	A	S
T	S	R	H	S	E	L	D	R	S
E	A	K	T	O	M	A	T	O	E

BACON
CARROT
CELERY
CHICKEN
CRAB
EGG SALAD
MAYONNAISE
SALMON
SARDINES
SAUSAGE
SHRIMP
SPAM
STEAK
TOMATOES
TUNA
TURKEY

Transcript of conversation between Detective Sergeant Katie McCrawley and Detective Constable Alex Summers, conducted via text message.

McCrawley: where r u?

Summers: hiding

McCrawley: what?

Summers: hiding with crime Scene techs. The museum people got mad about dummies being moved

Summers: *mummies

McCrawley: u r an idiot. Get bk here. Need u 2 distract the curators while we move things

Summers: why me????

McCrawley: because I said so?

Summers: fine. Easton has found something on the victim's corpse.

McCrawley: tell him we'll b over soon. also, tell him he dropped his scarf in the staff room. Jessops has it.

[END OF TRANSCRIPT]

When the police officers have *carefully* lifted up Mummy A to move it to the correct place, a piece of paper is found stuck to the floor. There's a code on it, but no one has been able to crack it yet. Can you help?

YFSFS OMGBD USGVG RMMNB UNIFJ
IKSDL NSGVD EDRGF DSFSF MILUY
YGHFJ LGHOK IKKLF FSKFF ESKJV
SUOJS ONHMS NERYI OKASS WJLUI
IGMAS TSFFH SSDGD TAWER IKILG
MITTF EDFVB FDBFH OXCVB RCVAS
YDBFB ODFGF UDFGD TDFFG OUILE
PADER AUHKS YDJNB

The keen eyes of the curators notice scuff marks on the floor that weren't there before, indicating that the displays have been moved. A look through the victim's desk uncovers an exhibit plan for the Egyptian area, but unfortunately it is in a code known only to the victim. Can you locate the position of each of the displays listed in the grid? What display covered the giant X marked on the floor?

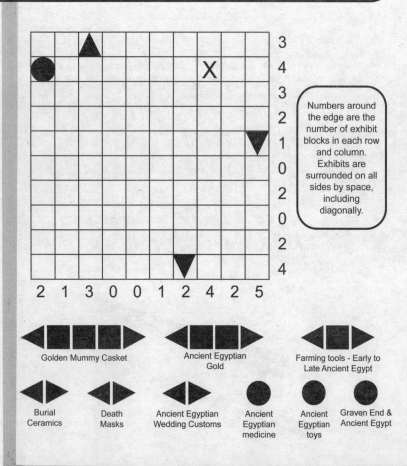

Numbers around the edge are the number of exhibit blocks in each row and column. Exhibits are surrounded on all sides by space, including diagonally.

Golden Mummy Casket

Ancient Egyptian Gold

Farming tools - Early to Late Ancient Egypt

Burial Ceramics

Death Masks

Ancient Egyptian Wedding Customs

Ancient Egyptian medicine

Ancient Egyptian toys

Graven End & Ancient Egypt

Summers points out that someone has scratched hieroglyphs into the side of one of the displays. Is it vandalism, or is someone leaving a message?

A	F	KH	K	E
A	M	KH CH	G	Y
I	N	SZ	T	U W
U W	R	S	TJ	M
B	H	SH	D	N
P	H	K	DJ	L

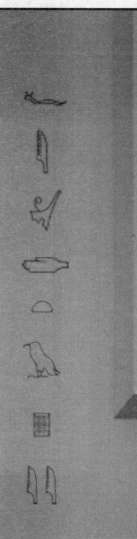

Sara's PUZZLE PAGES

Word Search: Hot Drinks

PUZZLE 135

S	A	E	T	N	E	E	R	G	H	A	G	E	T	A
R	E	D	I	C	E	L	P	P	A	F	V	M	Y	U
K	M	A	T	E	C	O	C	I	D	O	U	Y	D	U
N	Y	N	O	L	L	I	U	O	B	L	C	E	D	P
V	H	O	T	C	H	O	C	O	L	A	T	E	O	M
T	E	M	B	F	S	A	K	E	P	S	P	F	T	I
M	R	E	V	L	O	B	D	P	A	N	R	F	T	R
R	B	L	A	H	A	W	U	L	V	A	S	O	O	U
I	A	T	S	P	I	C	E	D	P	U	N	C	H	I
U	L	O	J	N	C	P	K	L	R	D	N	H	R	B
T	T	H	E	I	F	L	A	T	T	E	S	S	O	P
T	E	N	N	Y	R	R	E	B	E	L	A	I	P	A
V	A	O	S	S	E	R	P	S	E	A	V	R	I	A
Z	A	H	C	O	M	A	L	T	E	D	M	I	L	K
S	I	X	T	E	L	Q	X	R	L	S	O	T	Y	D

ALEBERRY	HERBAL TEA	MATE COCIDO
APPLE CIDER	HOT CHOCOLATE	MOCHA
BLACK TEA	HOT LEMONADE	MULLED WINE
BOUILLON	HOT TODDY	POSSET
CAPPUCCINO	IRISH COFFEE	SAKE
ESPRESSO	LATTE	SALEP
GREEN TEA	MALTED MILK	SPICED PUNCH

Codebreaker

PUZZLE
136

	11		9		23		23		8		24	
25	19	21	13	23	4	14	5		12	18	14	13
	19		2		9		15		14		20	
15	26	14	25		12	4	15	25	19	12	14	22
	15		4		5		24				25	
9	24	26	14	12	15	12		3	19	14	23	25
			13		12		21		18			
26	15	12	20	15		10	19	23	25	6	15	23
	22				17		12		26		16	
22	4	14	5	26	18	13	7		19	1	9	6
	19		19		19		26		24		22	
12	15	9	26		25	12	9	1	15	23	25	2
	24		5		15		13		24		23	

A B C D E F G H I J K L M N O P Q R S T U V W X Y Z

1	2	3	4	5	6	7	8	9	10	11	12	13
						K						

14	15	16	17	18	19	20	21	22	23	24	25	26
I							W					

CCTV footage from the time of the murder is conveniently missing. However, a still of the Egyptian gold display from before the murder shows discrepancies when compared to a photo taken by a Crime Scene Tech after the murder.

Can you find the **eight** differences
between the two photos?

Sara's PUZZLE PAGES

THE BEST-SELLING NEWSPAPER IN GRAVEN END

A - Z

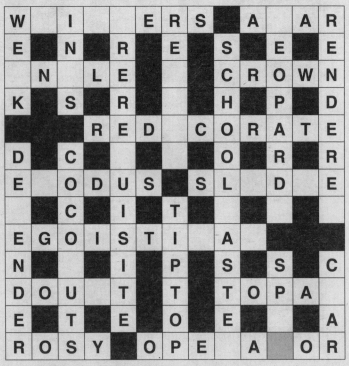

A B C D E F G H I J K L M N O P Q R S T U V W X Y Z

Crossword

PUZZLE
139

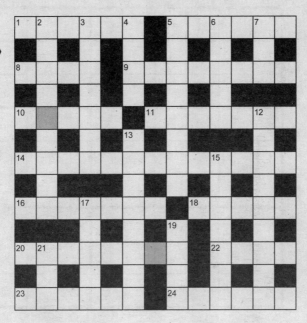

Across

1 Country in N Europe (6)
5 ___ Holden: English actress (6)
8 Island of Indonesia (4)
9 Quarrels (8)
10 Whip eggs (5)
11 Mislead on purpose (7)
14 Hidden store of valuables (8,5)
16 Declare to be true (7)
18 Small flexible bag (5)
20 Covered walk in a convent (8)
22 Snatched (4)
23 Subatomic particle such as a nucleon (6)
24 Saying (6)

Down

2 Worn by the elements (9)
3 Salt lake in the Jordan Valley (4,3)
4 Topical information (4)
5 Roused from sleep (8)
6 Standpoint (5)
7 Small numbered cube (3)
12 Full of life (9)
13 Metallic element used in light bulbs (8)
15 Male chicken (7)
17 Oneness (5)
19 Clench (4)
21 Mauna ___ : Hawaiian volcano (3)

Sara's PUZZLE PAGES

Letter-Doku!

PUZZLE 140

		H	F					D
F			I		H		A	
		D					I	
	G		E	A				
C								I
				I	C		G	
	B					H		
	E		C		D			G
I					B	E		

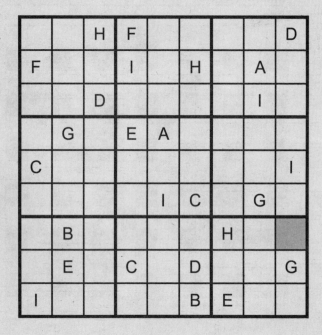

GRAVEN PROPERTIES

LETTING AND SALES
COMMERCIAL AND
RESIDENTIAL
PROPERTIES

ONE-STOP-POP-AND-SHOP

<ins>NOTICE TO CUSTOMERS:</ins>
We will be closed for
approximately one week due
to unforeseen circumstances.
We apologise for any
inconvenience caused and
look forward to seeing you
all again soon.

Kriss Kross

PUZZLE
141

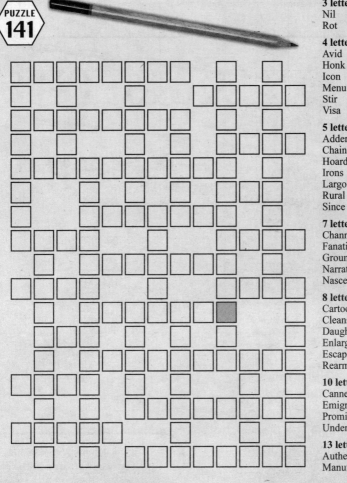

3 letters
Nil
Rot

4 letters
Avid
Honk
Icon
Menu
Stir
Visa

5 letters
Adder
Chain
Hoard
Irons
Largo
Rural
Since

7 letters
Channel
Fanatic
Grounds
Narrate
Nascent

8 letters
Cartoons
Cleanser
Daughter
Enlarged
Escapism
Rearmost

10 letters
Cannellone
Emigration
Prominence
Underlying

13 letters
Authentically
Manufacturers

Before Dr. Easton and the Crime Scene Techs arrive, McCrawley notices that there is a scrap of newspaper clutched in the victim's hand.
Someone has scribbled the word "FAKE" on it.

The New Gra

Friday, 14th August 2020

~~FAKE!!~~

Ancient Gold Found in Graven End

A precious hoard of 67 gold coins was unearthed in the grounds of the Graven End Manor by keen metal detectorist and local scientist, Doctor Leo Santana. Each of the coins have the head of a man and a date, 21 BCE, stamped on them, and weigh approximately 60g.

Matthew Jessup, owner of the Graven End Museum, which purchased the hoard from Dr. Santana for a large undisclosed sum, expressed his excitement at the find. "It's amazing to think that these Egyptian coins have been hiding in the grounds of our very own manor house for years with no one knowing."

"There hasn't been a significant gold find in this area for well over a hundred years," Jessup continued. "Not since the builders of the Graven End Theatre found the Kettle of Tunis. So, of course the museum wanted to snap them up".

The coins go on display at the end of the month and a special unveiling event for press and donors is being planned.

How does the victim know the coins were fake?

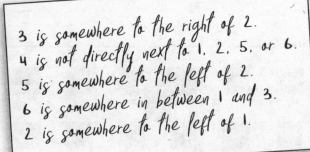

3 is somewhere to the right of 2.
4 is not directly next to 1, 2, 5, or 6.
5 is somewhere to the left of 2.
6 is somewhere in between 1 and 3.
2 is somewhere to the left of 1.

DISPLAY ORDER:

While waiting for Dr. Easton to examine the body,
something catches the eye of McCrawley: the scarabs
on the medicine display are out of order, and a
piece of paper has been left beside them. Can you work
out what order the scarabs are supposed to be in?

Sara's PUZZLE PAGES

THE BEST-SELLING NEWSPAPER IN GRAVEN END

Codebreaker

PUZZLE 144

1		9		22				21		10		23
7	23	5	18	21	7		13	18	17	4	7	19
24		4		18		5		19		3		19
18	24	10	20	5	23	22		24	3	4	26	23
4		4		1		4		7		24		12
7	23	23	12		19	3	24	25	23			
19		18		13		4		24		12		1
		14	24	18	22	1		16	23	7	5	
1		3		22		4		1		24		11
16	21	21	1	23		23	8	6	24	3	23	1
23		11		13		1		23		4		4
24	18	11	21	5	18		2	23	24	7	23	12
18		17		3				15		19		23

A B C D E F G H I J K L M N O P Q R S T U V W X Y Z

1	2	3	4	5	6	7	8	9	10	11	12	13

14	15	16	17	18	19	20	21	22	23	24	25	26
K								T				V

Pathfinder: Colours

PUZZLE 145

ALIZARIN
ASPARAGUS
BABY PINK
CADMIUM YELLOW
CAMEL
FUCHSIA
GOLDENROD
JASPER
KHAKI
NAVY BLUE
ORANGE
PERIWINKLE
PURPLE

U	I	M	S	A	J	A	U	F	K
M	A	D	P	E	E	I	C	I	H
Y	C	E	P	R	G	S	H	K	A
E	E	R	D	B	N	A	R	O	E
L	L	I	O	A	N	K	A	L	U
L	K	W	R	B	I	P	S	B	Y
O	N	I	N	Y	P	A	N	A	V
W	C	D	E	S	U	R	N	A	Z
M	A	L	O	G	G	A	I	R	I
E	L	P	U	R	P	L	E	A	L

Use this page to record any notes or answers for this crime. This may help you to determine who you think the killer is at the very end.

PUZZLE	ANSWER
113	
116	
117	
118	
119	
122	
125	
128	
129	
132	
133	
134	
137	
142	
143	

Did you notice anything strange about the puzzles in the Graven End newspaper?

The strength it would've taken to shove an amulet down Masterson's throat is interesting. Killer's anger at Masterson may have given them the strength. Anger's powerful.

And the killer is definitely angry at being called a liar again by Masterson.

What's the connection between the two?

They seem to know the area well – knew when no one but the curator would be in the museum. Summers thinks they're local, which looks likely. Leo Santana has appeared again.

I need to dig deeper on this.

CRIME SCENE
SIX

LOCATION:
Graven End
Forensic
Laboratory

MURDER WEAPON:
Poison

VICTIM:
Dr. Josie Denby

The sixth victim was a technician in Graven End Police department's own forensic laboratory. Having moved straight from university to the laboratory as a forensic technician just two months before her death, she was considered to be smart, even "exceptional" at her job by some of her colleagues, often "finding connections that no one else knew existed".

She worked extensively with Dr Easton's Crime Scene Techs, and spent weeks working on the ███████████████████████████████████████ ████████████████████████████████ and ██████ with ███████████████████████ in Little Graven.

She had frequent, often-unrelenting migraines, and colleagues mentioned that when she was alone in the lab, she would turn most of the overhead fluorescent lights off, preferring to work in softer lighting than the lab usually had. This could explain how the killer moved through the lab unnoticed by the victim.

The victim was found dead by one of her colleagues the following morning.

A torn print out of a DNA sequence is found underneath the victim's body. Can you determine if it is the same as the DNA the victim was studying at the time of her murder?

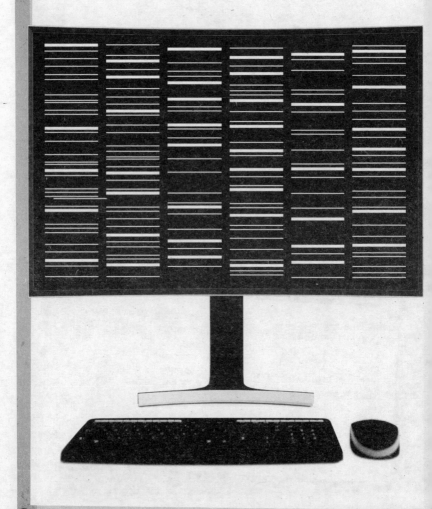

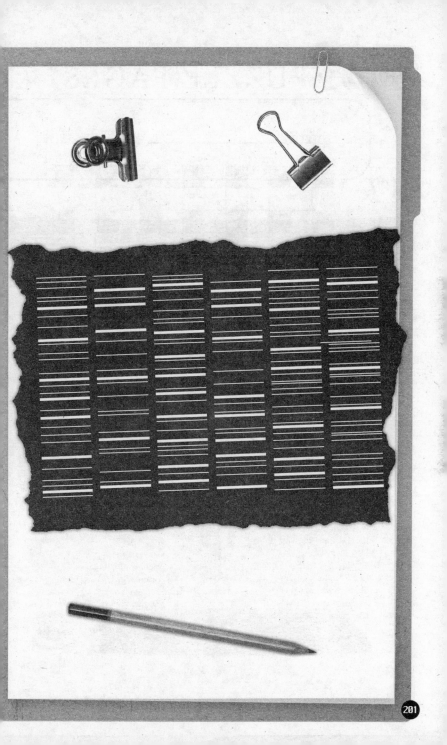

Sara's PUZZLE PAGES

THE BEST-SELLING NEWSPAPER IN GRAVEN END

Crossword

PUZZLE
147

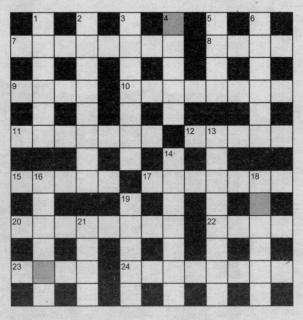

Across

7 Peacemaker (8)
8 Cereal grains (4)
9 Passionate desire for something (4)
10 Lacking knowledge (8)
11 Safe places (7)
12 Inferior to (5)
15 Religious groups (5)
17 Go backwards (7)
20 Muttered (8)
22 River in central England (4)
23 Not as much (4)
24 State of being the same (8)

Down

1 Coniferous tree (6)
2 Cause deliberate damage to (8)
3 Hopes to achieve (7)
4 Main stem of a tree (5)
5 Not sweet (4)
6 Causes a sharp pain (6)
13 Capable of being used (8)
14 Necessary (7)
16 Displayed freely (6)
18 Fires a bullet (6)
19 Small container (5)
21 Sentimentality (4)

A - Z

PUZZLE 148

A		A	R	■	D	E		I	R	I	■	M
P			■			■		N		N	■	I
P	R			I	E	S			U	S		
R	■	R		S		A		O		I	■	M
O		N			T		S	E	P	I	A
X				U	N				I		N
I		O		D				I		D	
M				G	R	A	F	T			G
A	D	D	L	E		F		A		P	I	E
T				M			B		I		M
E		A	D	E		O	B	L	I		U	E
L		L			R		E		U		N
	U	L	E		I	D	E	■	G		N	T

A B C D E F G H I J K L M N O P Q R S T U V W X Y Z

Even the hardest puzzles have a solution.

Sara's PUZZLE PAGES

Codebreaker

PUZZLE
149

1	10	26	21			12	11	12	14	10	21	18	21
18		10		21		17		15		24		18
25	10	23	22	22	18	9		12	1	17	21	18
10		6		17		7		1		6		22
23	19	3	18	1	13	23	19	12	11	6	8	
3				12		19		14		18		11
12	24	12	1	9	21		21	3	12	19	16	12
6		20		23		18		18				6
	14	17	19	14	18	19	3	1	12	3	18	9
21		6		12		2		23		10		19
7	19	17	6	6		17	11	21	18	1	5	18
10		3		6		23		18		4		21
12	6	6	12	8	23	19	26		12	21	7	21

A B C D E F G H I J K L M N O P Q R S T U V W X Y Z

1	2	3	4	5	6	7	8	9	10	11	12	13
R							Y					

14	15	16	17	18	19	20	21	22	23	24	25	26
C												

Pathfinder: Insurance Words

BACKING
BOND
CERTAINTY
COVER
DEED
INVESTMENT
PROVISION
SAFEGUARD
SECURITY
SUPPORT
TESTAMENT
UNDERWRITER
WARRANTY

C	E	G	U	A	R	R	O	V	I
T	R	E	F	A	D	P	E	T	S
R	T	A	I	S	E	M	S	R	I
O	P	T	N	T	N	A	T	E	O
U	P	Y	D	E	R	I	T	V	N
S	Y	B	N	U	W	R	E	O	I
I	T	O	E	D	N	A	R	C	N
R	U	N	E	Y	T	R	R	E	V
E	C	D	D	B	A	W	A	S	T
S	G	N	I	K	C	T	N	E	M

Graven End University's
ANNUAL BOOK SALE
THIS SAT & SUN, 10AM-4PM, CAMPUS LIBRARY
TEXT BOOKS • MAGAZINES • JOURNALS • & MORE | CASH ONLY, PLEASE

GRAVEN END
UNIVERSITY

This word search was found at the back of the victim's notebook. It seems like it's made up of DNA strands, but it also looks odd. Can you solve the word search and work out what's different about it?

Y	T	C	A	A	T	T	A	C	C	C	A	G	A
T	G	A	C	C	G	G	A	T	C	C	C	O	A
C	U	C	G	T	T	G	C	A	A	T	C	G	A
G	A	A	G	T	K	G	A	G	C	G	G	T	C
C	C	T	A	A	A	C	G	G	N	G	T	C	C
A	C	A	G	T	T	C	C	C	G	A	T	C	G
T	G	O	A	C	A	A	A	A	T	A	G	A	T
T	A	C	A	A	W	A	C	A	M	T	A	G	G
A	T	A	T	A	C	T	A	A	G	T	G	G	A
G	T	T	A	A	T	A	G	T	G	T	E	A	G
G	A	W	C	T	A	G	A	C	C	A	T	T	G
A	G	T	A	C	C	C	G	A	A	G	C	T	E
C	C	A	G	C	A	A	T	A	A	C	A	A	L
A	C	C	A	C	L	T	A	C	G	C	A	T	A

CCTGGAATTTA	AGCAATAACA	GTTACCAGATC
CCGATTAGCC	GACCCATTAAC	AATTAACGGAC
AGTTCCCGAT	TATTAGGACC	AAACCGTGAG
TACGATAACCG	TAGTACAAGT	CAGGATTACG
TGACCGGAT		TACCCGAAGC

The top drawer of the victim's desk is locked, and
the keypad looks strange - the numbers aren't the
typical 1-9, and the last number ism missing. So far,
the Crime Scene Techs have worked out that the first
three digits are **5**, **18** and **9**.

Can you work out
the final number?

2	3	5
6	9	15
18	27	

Sara's PUZZLE PAGES

THE BEST-SELLING NEWSPAPER IN GRAVEN END

Letter-Doku!

PUZZLE
153

Asserts to be the case	▼	Standards	▼	21st Greek letter	▼	Phantasm	▼	European country
Legal ambiguity ▶				▼				
Act of getting rid of	17th Greek letter ▶				Under judgement (3,6) ▶		Wife of a knight
▶						▼		▼
Type of savings account (abbrev)	Decorate		Fish ▶					
		Remains preserved in rock	▼	Auction offer ▶			
Hinged barriers	Expect; think that ▶	Repeat something once more	Handsome crow ▶				
▶	▼			Egyptian goddess		Wicked	Close securely; aquatic mammal
Disperse (anag)				▼			
Mentally sharp ▶							
Pile	Keys: US singer ▶						
▶			Exchange for money ▶				

208

Letter-Doku!

PUZZLE 154

G					I			
	A							G
E	I	D	B					
		I	F			C		
		C	H	I	G	B		
		H			C	D		
					D	E	B	A
D							C	
			E					D

"The closer you get, the further away the answer can seem."

The first thing the detectives notice as they finally open the drawer is that a photograph has been placed on top of the contents. On closer inspection, it becomes obvious that it is a photo of the very drawer they are looking in but with a few differences.

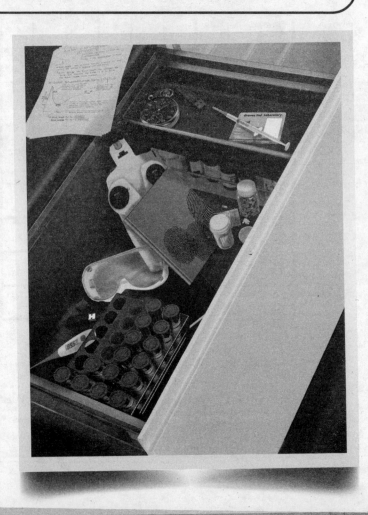

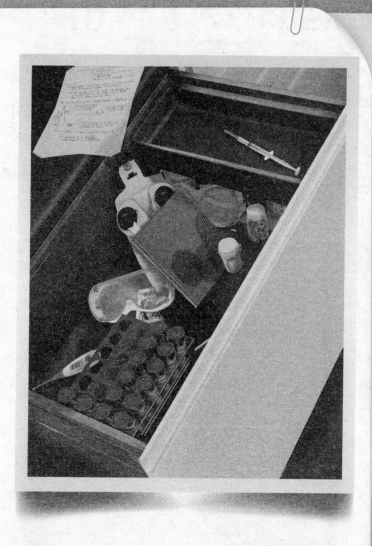

Can you find the **six** differences
between the two photos?

Sara's PUZZLE PAGES

THE BEST-SELLING NEWSPAPER IN GRAVEN END

Kriss Kross

PUZZLE 156

3 letters
Now
Sir

4 letters
Lens
When

5 letters
Astir
Fears
Fungi
Jetty
Khaki
Night
Rigid
Talon
Today
Valid

6 letters
Archer
Impede
Mohair
Sketch
Starch
Tinkle

7 letters
Sandals
Shallot

8 letters
Archival
Hitherto

11 letters
Aggravation
Awkwardness
Heavyweight
Imaginative
Inadvertent
Tetrahedron

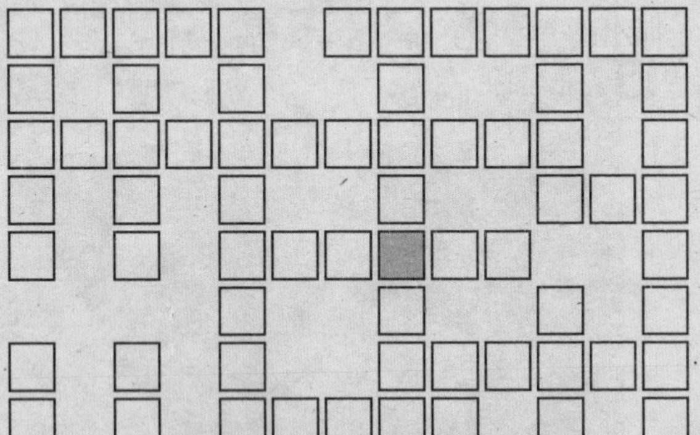

212

Word Search: Shades of Green

PUZZLE 157

```
C O M E S A J V L L A Z J T A
N L D I Q O I H C A T S I P C
T E C N N E E R G E L P P A I
I M E J E T L S O T Z A R R D
N F O R E S T G R E E N I I G
T S S U G A R A P S A K X S R
U G H U N T E R G R E E N G E
R L O E T I H C A L A M E R E
Q M F V J U N G L E G R E E N
U A R I D T G Y I L L I R E T
O N U L I S G O M R K U G N V
I T U O K R P H E S B Z K A R
S I I D E I S I R G I D R E V
E S U E R T R A H C R T A U I
M S N J H Z E A V O C A D O D
```

ACID GREEN	FOREST GREEN	MINT
APPLE GREEN	HUNTER GREEN	OLIVE
ASPARAGUS	JUNGLE GREEN	PARIS GREEN
AVOCADO	KELLY GREEN	PISTACHIO
BRIGHT GREEN	LIME	TEAL
CHARTREUSE	MALACHITE	TURQUOISE
DARK GREEN	MANTIS	VERDIGRIS

9 11 14 15 23 23 8 1 20 25 15 21
4 9 4.

25 15 21 4 15 14 ' 20 11 14 15 23
1 14 25 20 8 9 14 7.

9 11 14 15 23 5 14 15 21 7 8. 9 4
15 14 ' 20 21 14 4 5 18 19 20 1 14
4 23 8 25 23 15 21 12 4 25 15 21
4 15 20 8 9 19.

2 5 3 1 21 19 5 9 3 1 14.

6 9 14 5. 9 6 25 15 21 1 18 5 14
15 20 7 15 9 14 7 20 15 20 5 12
12 13 5 25 15 21 3 1 14 20 5 12
12 20 8 5 16 15 12 9 3 5.

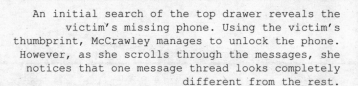

An initial search of the top drawer reveals the victim's missing phone. Using the victim's thumbprint, McCrawley manages to unlock the phone. However, as she scrolls through the messages, she notices that one message thread looks completely different from the rest.

Can you work out what the messages say?

A final sweep of the victim's top desk drawer reveals a sticky note with familiar handwriting on it. The officer on duty correctly identifies it as another riddle left by the killer, but is unable to find a solution. Can you?

Josie has 2 bottles of identical-looking tablets. She must take one tablet from each bottle every day: if she forgets to take one or takes more than one of either, she might be ill. When she has two days' supply left, she drops all four tablets on the floor, mixing them up.

What should poor Josie do?

Partial transcript of conversation between Detective McCrawley and Doctor Alan Easton, taken from the laboratory's autopsy room recorder.

McCrawley: So, anything for us, Doc?

Easton: Well, the body was found with minimal signs of trauma. A bruise on the back of the head, probably from where she collapsed, and Doctor Asher reported a faint odour present on the body at the scene. Internally, there were more extensive signs. Vomit was found in her lungs, and her pharynx was found partially collapsed. There were visible changes to the lining of the stomach and microscopic analysis revealed the start of cell death in her organs.

McCrawley: Right. What's your guess at cause of death?

Easton: I'd say poisoning, but we haven't had the toxicology screening back yet, I'm afraid.

McCrawley: Fits with the riddle we found. What's your best stab in the dark?

Easton: She worked with poisons, so mercury, potassium cyanide, warfarin or arsenic trioxide would be my guess.

[END OF TRANSCRIPT]

These 4 entries are from the Poisons Formulary, describing the physical effects of overdose. Can you use the information to work out the most likely poison used to kill the victim?

Arsenic Trioxide
Side effects: emanation of garlicky odour from the skin and muscosal linings; vomiting; significant constriction of the pharyngeal passageway; stomach muscosal membrane damage, evidenced by white particles in the membrane; organ failure.

Mercury
Side effects: erythematous rash; slight hepatic enlargement with mild constriction of the blood vessels causing delayed refill and blanching; damage to the muscosal membrane of the stomach, leading a change in colour to slate grey.

Potassium Cyanide
Side effects: vomiting; erythematous rash; significant pulmonary odema causing asphyxiation, myocardial infarction and cardiac cell death; emanation of bitter almond odour emanating from the skin and muscosal linings.

Warfarin
Side effects: significant internal bleeding leading to exsanguination and pulmonary collapse; bursting of epidermal blood vessels causing a petechiae rash; damage to the muscosal membrane of the stomach evidenced by yellowing.

PUZZLE
160

Sara's PUZZLE PAGES

THE BEST-SELLING NEWSPAPER IN GRAVEN END

Codebreaker

PUZZLE
161

21		24		10		17		17		15		15
20	6	3	5	12	20	6	6	20		17	20	2
26		24		17		15		20		3		18
20	14	15	2	6		6	7	18	1	15	13	7
4		1		3		12		17				1
	17	6	12	8	8	20	13		3	13	4	25
11		3		25				22		3		23
20	15	2	16		21	18	3	20	8	4	25	
25				23		20		13		12		18
9	3	1	21	15	4	4		4	3	6	18	20
15		20		12		3		7		3		12
13	7	6		19	3	19	15	2	3	7	12	17
17		17		20		20		11		1		20

A B C D E F G H I J K L M N O P Q R S T U V W X Y Z

1	2	3	4	5	6	7	8	9	10	11	12	13
	C											

14	15	16	17	18	19	20	21	22	23	24	25	26
	A			R								

218

Crossword

PUZZLE
162

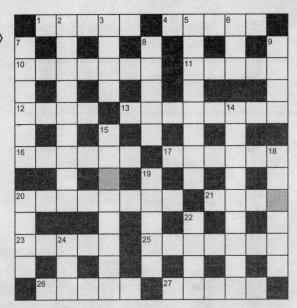

Across

1 ___ White: popular snooker player (5)
4 Covers in paper (5)
10 Become husky (of a voice) (7)
11 Juicy fruit (5)
12 Travelled by horse (4)
13 Airport checking devices (8)
16 Large terrestrial monkey (6)
17 Lofts (6)
20 Deep ditches (8)
21 Assist (4)
23 Acknowledged; assumed (5)
25 Ice statues with coal for eyes (7)
26 Block of wood (5)
27 Timber framework (5)

Down

2 Impossible to hear (9)
3 Wire lattice (4)
5 Chew cud (8)
6 Joke (3)
7 Winged child (6)
8 Bump (5)
9 Plant containers (4)
14 Layer of cells covering an organism (9)
15 Explosively unstable (8)
18 Lying on the back (6)
19 Robbery (5)
20 Pulls at (4)
22 Grey-haired with age (4)
24 Vessel (3)

This is a photo of the victim's desk taken just after the body is found. Does anything look strange to you?

HG AW EV VE
TY SO LU AT
ER MI NE DE
LS OU XO KP
FI LN SG YU
MN DO SE RL
AT KH WE
DQ ZE BS YK

?

Dr. Easton calls to say that they'd found a piece of paper in the victim's trouser pocket. He sends McCrawley a photo of it and she realises that they've seen this type of puzzle before. Try deleting one letter from each pair to decipher the killer's message.

Transcript of conversation between Detective Sergeant McCrawley and Detective Constable Alex Summers, conducted via text message.

McCrawley: finished with Easton. he says overdose but i think we go with poisoning

Summers: ok. found something else. a USB taped underneath her desk

McCrawley: and???

Summers: password. need a 4-digit code

McCrawley: Is there a puzzle?

Summers: oh yep. a maze

McCrawley: great. getting sick of puzzles now

[END OF TRANSCRIPT]

Does the maze reveal anything about the password for the USB?

Arrow Words

PUZZLE 166

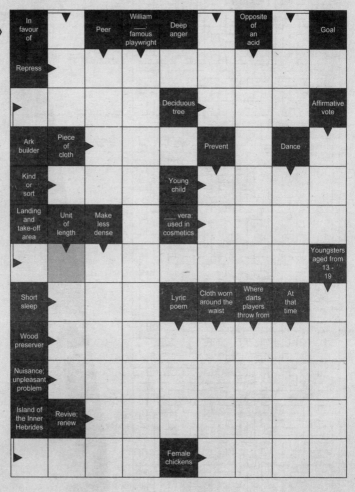

Clues within the grid:

- In favour of
- Peer
- William ___: famous playwright
- Deep anger
- Opposite of an acid
- Goal
- Repress
- Deciduous tree
- Affirmative vote
- Ark builder
- Piece of cloth
- Prevent
- Dance
- Kind or sort
- Young child
- Landing and take-off area
- Unit of length
- Make less dense
- ___ vera: used in cosmetics
- Youngsters aged from 13 - 19
- Short sleep
- Lyric poem
- Cloth worn around the waist
- Where darts players throw from
- At that time
- Wood preserver
- Nuisance; unpleasant problem
- Island of the Inner Hebrides
- Revive; renew
- Female chickens

" When nothing make sense, just keep going. "

A - Z

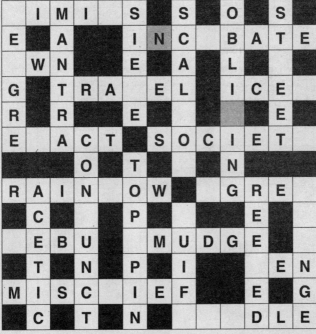

A B C D E F G H I J K L M N O P Q R S T U V W X Y Z

PUZZLE 168

The USB stick contains a single file: a scan of a page from the National Poisons Register, which lists the details of people purchasing restricted substances. It is something the victim would have had access to.

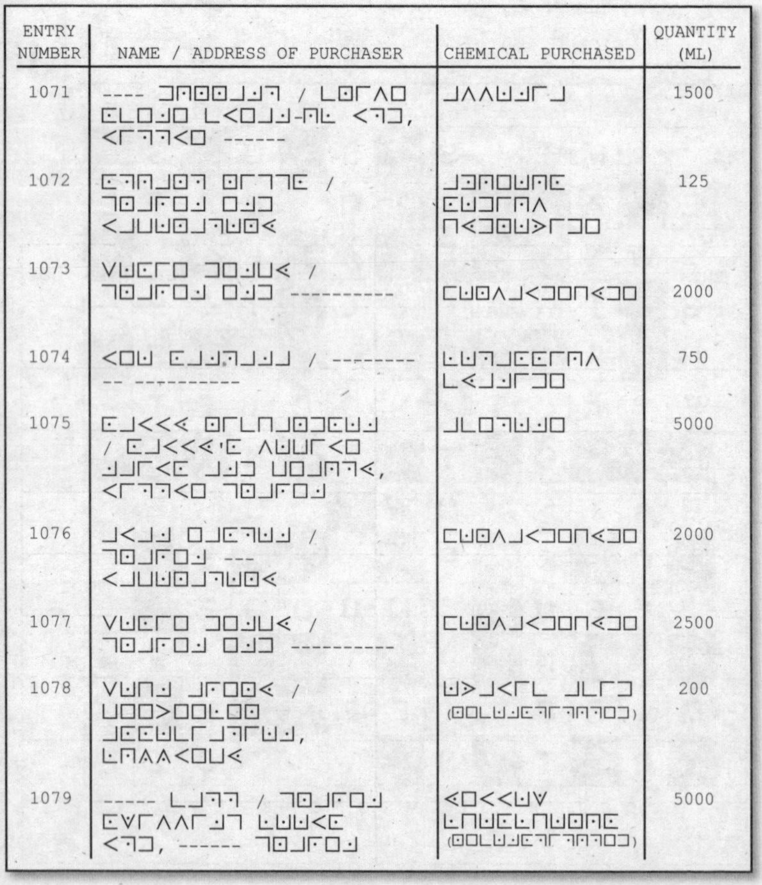

ENTRY NUMBER	NAME / ADDRESS OF PURCHASER	CHEMICAL PURCHASED	QUANTITY (ML)
1071	[illegible]	[illegible]	1500
1072	[illegible]	[illegible]	125
1073	[illegible]	[illegible]	2000
1074	[illegible]	[illegible]	750
1075	[illegible]	[illegible]	5000
1076	[illegible]	[illegible]	2000
1077	[illegible]	[illegible]	2500
1078	[illegible]	[illegible]	200
1079	[illegible]	[illegible]	5000

Unfortunately, the file is corrupted and only parts of it are able to be restored. Unrecoverable data has been replaced with a -. The Techs recover what they can, but can you work out the rest?

```
⌐ ⊔ L ⊐ ◻ ⊏ ⌐ ⊓ ⌐ V > < ∧
A  B  C  D  E  F  G  H  I  J  K  L  M

⌐ ⊔ L. ⊐ ◻ ⊏ ⌐ ⊓ ⌐ V > < ∧
N  O  P  Q  R  S  T  U  V  W  X  Y  Z
```

ENTRY	NAME ON REGISTER	CHEMICAL/S PURCHASED
1071		
1072		
1073		
1074		
1075		
1076		
1077		
1078		
1079		

Sara's PUZZLE PAGES

THE BEST-SELLING NEWSPAPER IN GRAVEN END

" Piece by piece, the answer becomes clear. "

PUZZLE
169

Word search: London Road Names

R	T	E	E	R	T	S	D	N	O	B	R	O	T	D
S	T	I	H	A	T	T	O	N	G	A	R	D	E	N
P	E	P	A	V	A	H	W	S	P	Y	D	A	E	C
T	E	E	R	T	S	Y	N	A	B	L	A	O	R	H
E	R	C	L	F	D	A	I	V	L	I	O	R	T	E
E	T	A	E	R	A	W	N	O	I	S	R	E	S	Y
R	S	L	Y	I	O	S	G	Y	N	R	S	D	N	N
T	N	P	S	T	R	N	S	P	D	O	G	Y	O	E
S	Y	N	T	H	N	E	T	L	R	A	N	L	T	W
D	M	A	R	S	I	E	R	A	O	D	I	C	X	A
R	R	G	E	T	G	U	E	C	A	V	K	E	A	L
O	E	O	E	R	L	Q	E	E	D	R	M	X	C	K
F	J	D	T	E	E	R	T	S	T	N	E	G	E	R
X	B	A	K	E	R	S	T	R	E	E	T	Y	Z	T
O	Z	C	G	T	E	N	A	L	Y	R	U	R	D	C

ALBANY STREET
BAKER STREET
BAYLIS ROAD
BOND STREET
CAXTON STREET
CLYDE ROAD
CADOGAN PLACE
CHEYNE WALK
DOWNING STREET
DRURY LANE
ELGIN ROAD
FRITH STREET
HARLEY STREET
HATTON GARDEN
JERMYN STREET
KING'S ROAD
LIND ROAD
OXFORD STREET
QUEENSWAY
REGENT STREET
SAVOY PLACE

Kriss Kross

PUZZLE 170

3 letters	7 letters
Era	Abolish
Van	Animate
	Cameras
4 letters	Sawyers
Auks	
Chic	**8 letters**
Dewy	Niceness
Lost	Nominate

5 letters	9 letters
Aside	Distances
Gulfs	Leasehold
	Newsreels
6 letters	Paintings
Alcove	
Bobcat	**10 letters**
Erases	Felicitous
Hazier	Rendezvous
Houses	
Iguana	
Lyrics	
Novels	
Pallid	
Picnic	

Use this page to record any notes or answers for this crime. This may help you to determine who you think the killer is at the very end.

PUZZLE	ANSWER
146	
151	
152	
155	
158	
159	
163	
164	
165	
168	

Did you notice anything strange about the puzzles in the Graven End newspaper?

_____

_____

Damn it. I liked Josie.

Another overdose, this time with her own migraine medication. The killer must have medical knowledge to have known how much cyanide would be enough to kill.

Where does Leo Santana fit it in to all this?

There's something I'm missing...

I think we're getting closer, though. The clues are a mess, but we think it definitely has to be someone who knew and, possibly, worked with Josie, though we're not sure about that last bit yet.

I need to go over all the evidence one last time and start making connections.

It's time to end this.

Case Notes

Use these pages to record any notes or
observations you have about the case.

Turner: Summers, please refrain from wasting our time with ridiculous "memes".

Summers: Sorry, sir. was just excited that we're closing in on the puzzle killer

Charlton: nice job, guys

Nielson: wtg :)

Charlton: so, who is it???

Summers: all will b revealed!

McCrawley: its not a circus, summers

Turner: I'm not entirely sure about that...

McCrawley: Oh, ur funny, sir.

McCrawley: Ok Summers, lets catch this SOB.

Turner: Excuse me?

McCrawley: Oops. sorry, sir. lets catch this terrible person?

Turner: Go do your job, McCrawley.

Turner: And, Summers? Any more "memes" and you're suspended. I don't care what HR says.

[END OF TRANSCRIPT]

You've read through every case file related to the Puzzle Murders that the Graven End Police Department has. You've worked through each puzzle and read every taunting note, pored over all the statements and the discussions between members of the investigating team.

Some detectives will talk about "their gut feeling" and there is scientific evidence that suggests a gut feeling is a very real thing. You may have had a gut feeling early on, a sneaking suspicion that one person's actions and words don't quite add up, or that someone may not be what they seem. **Do you still have that gut feeling now?**

Other detectives are more analytical, eschewing emotion, choosing to focus purely on what the evidence says. Perhaps some of the evidence has been consistently pointing at a particular person. Maybe this evidence, when viewed within the context of all six murders, spells out the killer. **What is the evidence telling you?**

Now is the time for you to put your skills to the ultimate test: **decide who you think is the The Puzzle Killer.**

I think the killer is:

_____

CONCLUSION

It was Leo Santana who killed all these people. But Leo Santana doesn't exist any more.

There was once a man called Leo Santana. He was born and raised in Little Graven by Jorge and Michelle Santana. He was an excellent student and went to university in Graven End, where he studied biology with a view to eventually becoming a doctor. However, in Santana's last year, the university discovered that a lot of his final thesis had been stolen from an old scientific journal. It was a scandal. Leo Santana was kicked out of university for plagiarism. The notoriety drove him and his parents out of Little Graven, far away from all who knew them.

Secretly, Leo vowed revenge against the university and everyone who mocked him. Enter Doctor Alan Easton, forty-five years later. If you haven't already, look carefully at his name: it's an anagram of Leo Santana. The years had not been kind to Santana and his mental state had suffered greatly.

A wrong pizza order, delivered by Josh Harker, was the starting point for this senseless murder spree. Once Josh had died, Santana finally started to take revenge on those who had wronged him.

Daniel Jones was part of the team who discovered Santana's plagiarism (see the newspaper article on page 9) and Santana blamed him for destroying his life.

Hetty Merryweather, like Josh, was simply in the wrong place at the wrong time.

Sydney Blackstone, aka Joe Fraiser, was the other student involved in the scandal, although his name was never released. His fraudulent ways continued into adulthood, and Santana discovered his sideline in fake champagne. Still angry that Fraiser got to remain anonymous when Santana's name was smeared across the paper, Santana killed him.

When the coins were brought to the museum, Dr. Anthony Fraiser remembered the name "Santana", put two and two together, realised the coins were fake and confronted Santana in the museum. Unfortunately, that didn't end well for him.

The last victim, Josie Denby, was the closest to the killer, having worked with him since her transfer to the Graven End Laboratory. She handled all the evidence and realised who the killer was before anyone else. Her attempt to reach out to Santana, to understand, meant that her death was inevitable.

FOR YOUR EYES
ONLY:

SOLUTIONS

CRIME 1: JOSH HARKER

PUZZLE 1

The blacked-out letters spell
I DONT LIKE MUSHROOMS

PUZZLE 2

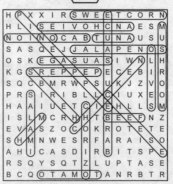

PEPPERONI is in the list
of words to find, but is
not in the word search.

PUZZLE 3

PUZZLE 4

PUZZLE 6

```
W R P O E M S   E   C
A   A S H   L   P F F O C R
R E V Y E R   F O E S
D A L L E V I A T E S
E G U E N C   C E
N E E   M   N I G H T   N
  S       T   U N
S   F A T H E R L A N D
U S   O   V       L O
B E T T E R M E N T   S
M A   U         P
A T H O R N   B   L Y E
R I   R   C U A Y
I S Y N T H E T I C E
N O T   A I A   E E L
E   I T E   N I B I D
S C   E N S U E   O D
```

PUZZLE 7

3	2	6	9	4	1	8	7	5
8	4	3	7	5	2	6	1	9
1	7	5	6	2	8	9	3	4
4	9	7	5	1	6	2	8	3
6	8	2	3	7	9	4	5	1
5	1	9	8	3	4	7	2	6
2	5	1	4	6	7	3	9	8
7	6	8	1	9	3	5	4	2
9	3	4	2	8	5	1	6	7

PUZZLE 8

```
 8.25  - Meat Feast to Short Lane
 8.30  - Pepperoni (with mushrooms) to Polaris Road
 8.40  - Meat Feast and Vegetarian to Avonvale Rise
 8.45  - 2 BBQ to Graven Meadows
 8.50  - 2 Vegetarian, Vegan, Margherita, and 2 Meat
          Feast to Rhoilla Close
 9.15  - Hawaiian (with Bacon), Margherita, and 2 Meat
          Feast to Church Lane East
 9.25  - 2 Margherita and 2 BBQ to Makkah Close
 9.35  - BBQ (no Pepperoni) to Orchardside
 9.40  - Meat Feast and 2 Pepperoni to Fairfield Square
 9.45  - Vegetarian and Pepperoni to Fairfield Square
10.05  - 3 Pepperoni, 2 Vegetarian, 4 BBQ, and 2 Vegan
          to Campus Avenue
10.15  - 2 Margherita, Pepperoni, and Hawaiian to Manor
          Road
10.25  - Pepperoni (with bacon and mushrooms) and
          Pepperoni to Avonvale Rise
10.30  - Pepperoni and Meat Feast to Dawes Close

          The murder was committed around 8.50pm.
```

PUZZLE 9

```
C O R N   G L O(W)W O R M
R   E   A   A   H   R   I
Y E A R D O T   E P I C S
P   R   M   E   E   G   C
T E M P O   S E L F I S H
O     N   T   B   N   I
G O B L I N   H A S S L E
R   O   S   P   R     V
A N O T H E R   R O N D O
P   K   M   O   O   I   U
(H)A L V E   N E W N E S S
E   E   N   T   S   C   L
R O T A T I O N   D E F Y
```

PUZZLE 10

```
Y I E L D S   N   B O B
  N     E   O P E R(A)  R
S T A L E S T   X   R   U
  R     R   T   T U R F S
C U R T S I E D   A     Q
  D   K   R   E   G   U
R E J O I N   S N E E Z E
A   I   N   S   C   O
I   N   C H O I R B O Y
N I G H(T)  O   R   L
B   L   R   R U C T I I O N
O   E V I C T   L     G
W A S   M     Z E P H Y R
```

PUZZLE 11

The number 8. On its side it's the symbol for infinity; cut in half, it's 0.

8

9

8

8; it's the number of letters in the number's word.

PUZZLE 12

```
S H R E D D E D   W O A D
P   H   E   Y     R   E
A M I G O   R E M O D E L
N   N   D   I       A   E
  A   E   E T C H I N G
(P O L A R I S)  U   N   A
O   A     A   R       T
T   B   N   T H I S T L E
T R E S T L E   O   R   E
E   H   N       S   U   A
R E A C T E D   I N D E X
E   L     E     T   G   E
D A F T   G R E Y N E S S
```

The killer wants us to pay attention to the word **POLARIS.** There is a Polaris Road on the map at the beginning, and Dr. Alan Easton lives on it.

The Morse code message is **I WILL BE BACK VERY SOON BUT I WONT BE THE SAME PERSON.**

PUZZLE
14

PUZZLE
15

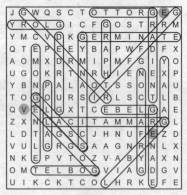

PUZZLE
16

PUZZLE
17

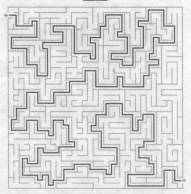

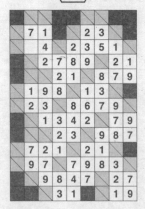

Puzzle 18

T	E	G	R	O	E	G	Y	D	N
O	U	R	N	K	N	B	G	S	A
W	B	G	A	L	I	I	I	B	R
N	S	F	R	P	M	R	C	V	E
L	R	E	I	H	E	M	H	I	R
A	V	Y	S	M	T	T	W	C	K
R	E	D	L	I	E	L	O	U	D
G	U	T	L	I	R	T	O	N	A
N	G	A	R	N	A	B	D	R	Y
E	F	A	R	G	T	O	N	S	M

Puzzle 19

30	29	28	27	26	22	21	10	9	8
31	33	34	40	41	25	23	20	11	7
32	35	39	42	50	51	24	19	12	6
36	38	43	49	55	54	52	18	13	5
37	44	48	58	57	56	53	17	14	4
45	47	59	87	86	85	83	16	15	3
46	60	88	93	94	96	84	82	1	2
61	67	89	92	95	99	97	81	79	77
62	66	68	90	91	100	98	80	78	76
63	64	65	69	70	71	72	73	74	75

The next clue is in square **61**.

Puzzle 20

Key number 2 is the correct key to the door. The order (from left to right) is: 3, 1, 5, 2, 4.

Puzzle 21

	C	H	I	V	E		O	S	I	E	R	
G		Y		A		J		H		R		E
R	E	P	U	L	S	E		E	X	A	L	T
I		O		E		E		A				C
L	O	C	K		A	P	P	R	O	A	C	H
L		R		M		S		E		N		
E	L	I	X	I	R		C	R	U	T	C	H
		S		S		B		S		I		O
A	N	Y	W	H	E	R	E		A	Q	U	A
D			M		I		D		U		R	
Z	E	B	R	A		E	M	E	R	A	L	D
E		A		S		F		N		R		S
	I	T	C	H	Y		S	T	A	Y	S	

PUZZLE 22

```
E N J O Y   P A D L O C K
A U E   U   E   F   I N
R A D I A N T   G   F   D
N   G   R   T   R E E   D
I E N   R E I N   L   I
N   M   S K Y   E C H I N G
G E E     N   I S L E   N
S   N O V A           G
  T   P E T   P
        O U R S   S
A   T R I C H   W   E L K
H U E   O   U S E   U   E
L   T A X I   X   D   L
E   S   C   B   O   O E
T   I   O E X T I N C T
I   N   M E   I Y   A
C H A M B E R   C A M E L
```

PUZZLE 23

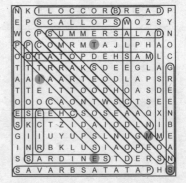

Make the **number three** with the buttons, leaving **four** of them untouched.

1	2	3
4	5	6
7	8	9
10	11	12
13	14	15

PUZZLE 24

Delete one letter from the pair to make the following message: **IVE SAID NO MUSHROOMS SO MANY TIMES IT WAS HIS OWN FAULT**

PUZZLE 25

```
G   G   A       Z O   G
A V E N U E   H O W L E R
T   A   G   S   O   D   A
H A R V E S T   L E E K S
E   B   R   A   O   R   P
R O O K   F R O G S
S   X   J   T   Y   B   S
    Q U A L M   C E N T
S   P   N   I   V   N   U
K H A K I   N E A R E S T
I   S   P   G   C   F   T
M O T L E Y   L U P I N E
P   Y   R       A   T   R
```

PUZZLE 26

```
N K I L O C C O R B R E A D P
E P S C A L L O P S W O Z S Y
W C P S U M M E R S A L A D N
P P C O M R M T A J L P H A O
O O A T O P D E H S A M L C
T T R R A K S D E E G L A G
A I A A R T E O D L A P S R
T E L T T O O D H O A S D E
O O C A O N T W S C T S E E
E S E E H C S O S E A A Q X N
S K C T Z I D A I O D L N I B
G I I U Y U P S L N U G M M E
I N R B K L U S I A O P E O A
S S A R D I N E S T D E R S N
S A V A R B S A T A T A P H S
```

CRIME 2: DANIEL JONES

```
       casipnmurt = manuscript
oilsfcstniacai = classification
         lietts = titles
       slhscroa = scholars
      aiailbrrn = librarian
       vhriscae = archives
      oxetbtkos = textbooks
        gnenldi = lending
```

The only location listed is the **archives**.

The correct time of death is **9 pm**.

Use the first letter of each book title to spell out
I COULD HAVE BEEN GREAT.

PUZZLE
34

Vol. 46 (4), 2014, pp. 465-472
International Journal of Evidence-Based Justice Reform

The key is in the stomach - rethinking current PMI estimations and methods of taking temperatures from cadavers

Leo Santana
Department of Biology, Graven End University
leo.santana@geu.edu

GRAVEN END
UNIVERSITY

Abstract: Currently, "PMI estimation approach holds little value when applied to human remains in real criminal investigation," (Sutherland, et al., 2003), but a review of the current methods, both controversial and widely accepted, of determining cadaveric temperature immediately post-mortem reveals new ways of calculating PMI estimations, allowing forensic teams to better assist law enforcement.

Keywords: thermoregulation, soup, tissue dehydration, cadaveric spasm, PMI

1. INTRODUCTION

The body maintains a constant internal temperature of approximately 37°C (98.6°F), the optimum temperature for the thousands of chemical reactions needed for life. As brain-death occurs, so does the cessation of autonomic body functions. The hypothalamus, which controls the homoeostatic feature of thermoregulation, ceases to function, and the temperature of the cadaver in question begins to rise, syncing with the ambient temperature of the area in which death occurred. This cooling is known as algor mortis.

Research carried out by Al-Alousi, et al. in 2002, shows that there can be a delay of up to three hours post-mortem before the temperature of the cadaver begins to drop, which contrasts with the widely accepted rate of a 1°C (33.8°F) decrease per hour. Also, this accepted measurement does not take into account external factors: the position of the cadaver (is it in the foetal position?), the location (bodies in subzero temperatures will reach an environmental equilibrium at a faster rate than those in humid climates), the presence of clothing (temperature

difference can be caused by the cadaver being clothed in a shirt or a well-insulated jacket), and the condition of the cadaver pre-mortem (an emaciated body is less insulated than an obese one).

It also does not account for the pre-mortem temperature of the cadaver, as someone who has been out in the elements for hours during a snowy December would have a lower internal temperature than one who had been indoors during the same period. Newton's Law of Cooling is inefficient, as these factors can not be input into the equation. The accuracy with which post-mortem temperature can currently be calculated remains less than is preferred for a reliable forensic pathological opinion.

This article will look at various methods that can be applied to cadavers in order to obtain a much more accurate temperature at the time of death. By gaining more knowledge in this area, we will be able to offer more precise COD recommendations and give better assistance to law enforcement officials.

2. THE SOUP METHOD

One controversial but widely used way of obtaining cadaveric temperature is the soup method. The pathologist uses a 23 cm (9 in) glass needle and carefully inserts it

PUZZLE 35

H	U	M	P	B	A	C	K		S	K	U	A
O		O		U	H	C		I	C			C
S	P	O	R	T		I		O	W	N	E	R
E		N		T		N		N	D			I
		J	E	T	T	I	S	O	N	E	D	
N		E		R		Z		E	E			I
E	X	P	O	S	E		P	R	E	S	E	T
W		I		C		R		V	S			Y
C	O	L	L	O	Q	U	I	Ⓐ	L			
O		O		T		S		T	M			F
M	A	G	I	C	S		O	R	I	B	I	
E		U		H		I		R	Ⓝ			N
R	E	E	K		L	A	D	Y	L	I	K	E

PUZZLE 36

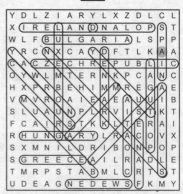

PUZZLE 37

The riddle is pointing to **The Elephant's Castle**.

PUZZLE 38

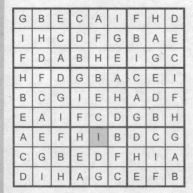

G	B	E	C	A	I	F	H	D
I	H	C	D	F	G	B	A	E
F	D	A	B	H	E	I	G	C
H	F	D	G	B	A	C	E	I
B	C	G	I	E	H	A	D	F
E	A	I	F	C	D	G	B	H
A	E	F	H	I	B	D	C	G
C	G	B	E	D	F	H	I	A
D	I	H	A	G	C	E	F	B

PUZZLE 39

	K	N	I	T	S		C	R	A	F	T	
A		O		E		A		E		O		P
D	E	C	O	R	U	M		M	O	G	U	L
O		T		M		U		O				U
R	O	U	T		A	S	S	U	M	I	N	G
E		R		L		E		N		N		
S	E	N	S	Ⓢ	E	S		S	T	A	G	E	D
		A		S		S		S		E		E
D	E	L	U	S	I	O	N		S	N	I	P
O				E		L		D		U		O
G	R	A	I	N		Ⓐ	I	R	P	O	R	T
S		Y		E		R		N		U		S
	W	E	E	D	S		B	O	O	S	T	

PUZZLE 40

PUZZLE 41

When reorganized, the letters from PUZZLE 40 spell out **The Codex Chrisicus**, which was one of the titles on the shelf of PUZZLE 31.

PUZZLE 42

PUZZLE 43

```
  B   E       W       A
N A N N Y   L A S A G N E
  L   T     A   T   U A
C L A R I N E T     T A C K
  P   A     N   A   H O
S A M P L E   G R E E N S
  R       X       E N D
S K I D D E D   S T R A Y
E   E   S   C   I     E
C A R V E   C O N C E P T
I   E   S     M     R
S L A L O M   P R I S E S
M   O   E     U   R D
H E L P   L I T T O R A L
  N   E   L   E   N T
S T U D I E D   P I L O T
  S   D       C   R
```

PUZZLE 44

The correct ISBN is **9784677834221**. It is in the list of ISBNs to find, but it is not in the word search.

6	5	3	8	2	4	9	7	1
9	8	2	7	1	6	3	5	4
1	4	7	9	5	3	6	2	8
3	9	4	5	8	7	1	6	2
7	6	8	2	4	1	5	3	9
2	1	5	3	6	9	8	4	7
5	7	9	4	3	8	2	1	6
4	2	6	1	9	5	7	8	3
8	3	1	6	7	2	4	9	5

The numbers in the highlighted squares are 1, 9, and 4. The next clue is on **page 194**.

PUZZLE 46

PUZZLE 47

PUZZLE 48

37	36	35	34	33	32	2	3	4	5
38	40	41	76	77	78	31	1	7	6
39	42	75	96	89	88	79	30	9	8
43	74	95	97	99	90	87	80	29	10
44	73	94	100	98	91	86	81	28	11
45	69	72	93	92	85	82	62	27	12
46	68	70	71	84	83	63	61	26	13
47	53	67	66	65	64	60	25	20	14
48	52	54	57	58	59	24	21	19	15
49	50	51	55	56	23	22	18	17	16

The next clue is on
page 95.

PUZZLE 49

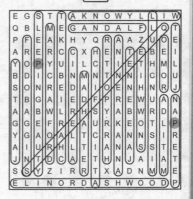

PUZZLE 50

```
    J   U   S   A   S   P
Q U E N C H   R O T A R Y
    R   E   A   G   A   E
L Y N X   D R U M B E A T
    C   I   E   I   M
S O M E O N(E)  B L O B S
    D   P   G   F   I   L
V O L T S   J O U S T E R
    M   I   M   R   A
M E S O Z O I C   T I C K
    T   N   O   E   I   R
R E T A I N   P H O T O N
    R   L   S   S   N   W
```

PUZZLE 51

Decrypting the passage of The Codex Chrisicus reveals the following message: **YOU HELPED TO RUIN MY FAMILY YOU DESERVE ALL OF THIS.**

PUZZLE 52

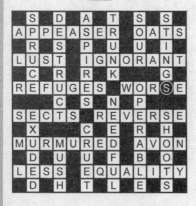

```
  S   D   A   T   S   S
A P P E A S E R   O A T S
  R   S   P   U   U   I
L U S T   I G N O R A N T
  C   R   R   K   G
R E F U G E S   W O R S(E)
  C   S   N   P
S E C T S   R E V E R S E
  X   C   E   R   H
M U R M U R E D   A V O N
  D   U   U   F   B   O
L E S S   E Q U A L I T Y
  D   H   T   L   E   S
```

PUZZLE 53

```
H O W L E R   O P A Q U E
O   A   L   O   A   U   X
C O X C O M B   Y   A E
K   W   P   S P R A Y E R
E R(O)D E   T   O       T
Y   R       I   L A S T S
    K   A N N U L   O
R U S T S   A     R   M
E       S   T   F R O Z E
J U S T I C E   E   R   R
O   H   G   L E V Y I N(G)
I   O   N   Y   E   T E
N E W E S T   P R E Y E D
```

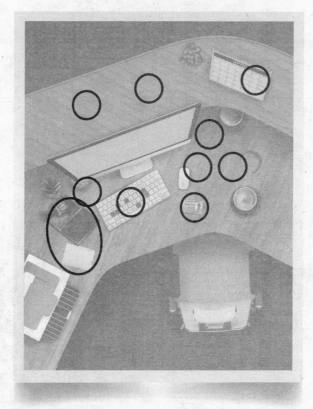

MESSAGE IN THE GRAVEN END
NEWSPAPER PUZZLES:

LEO SANTANA IS A MIXED UP PERSON

CRIME 3: HETTY MERRYWEATHER

PUZZLE 55

PUZZLE 56

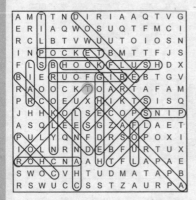

254

PUZZLE 57

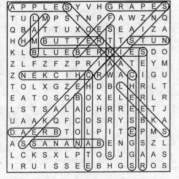

Yes, all of the items on the receipt can be found in the word search.

PUZZLE 58

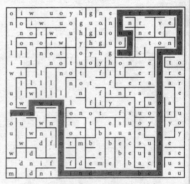

The correct path through the maze spells out the following message: **YOU WILL NOT FIND ME BECAUSE YOU ARE NOT CLEVER ENOUGH**

PUZZLE 59

PUZZLE 60

G	F	D	B	H	C	A	E	I
H	A	E	I	F	D	G	C	B
B	I	C	A	E	G	D	F	H
E	C	A	H	B	I	F	D	G
F	D	B	G	A	E	I	H	C
I	H	G	D	C	F	E	B	A
D	E	H	C	G	A	B	I	F
C	G	F	E	I	B	H	A	D
A	B	I	F	D	H	C	G	E

These footprints are not in the list of identified people. They must belong to the killer.

T	A	C	E	L	O	P	R	E	G
W	R	C	T	E	G	O	A	T	I
O	A	C	I	L	P	O	E	O	T
L	F	F	V	O	A	R	L	X	E
F	X	O	T	N	C	D	N	E	E
E	E	L	H	A	H	I	A	N	Z
R	O	E	P	H	I	M	P	K	B
R	O	G	N	C	P	M	U	N	E
E	R	A	A	K	N	O	B	R	A
T	C	A	M	E	L	S	I	E	V

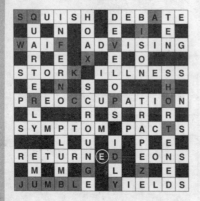

S	Q	U	I	S	H		D	E	B	A	T	E
	U		N		O		E		I		E	
W	A	I	F		A	D	V	I	S	I	N	G
	R		E		X		E		O			
S	T	O	R	K		I	L	L	N	E	S	S
	E		N		S		O				H	
P	R	E	O	C	C	U	P	A	T	I	O	N
	L		R		S		R		R			
S	Y	M	P	T	O	M		P	A	C	T	S
		L		U		I		P		E		
R	E	T	U	R	N	E	D		E	O	N	S
	M		M		G		L		Z		E	
J	U	M	B	L	E		Y	I	E	L	D	S

5	4	3	2	1	25	26	27	28	29
6	8	9	10	24	97	100	33	32	30
7	12	11	23	96	99	98	92	34	31
13	15	16	22	95	94	93	91	83	35
14	17	21	61	88	89	90	84	82	36
18	20	60	62	87	86	85	81	72	37
19	59	63	77	78	79	80	73	71	38
55	58	64	66	76	75	74	70	45	39
54	56	57	65	67	68	69	46	44	40
53	52	51	50	49	48	47	43	42	41

The car is parked in **space 57**. Turn the book upside down and the numbers read 61, 60, 59, 58, 57 and 56.

C	R	B			P	F		A
O	V	E	R	L	Y		B	O	X	I	N	G
R		W		U		I		C		Z		L
D	I	A	G	R	A	M		K	A	Z	O	O
I		R		T		P		E		Y		W
A	I	D	E		Q	U	I	T	S		S
L		S		P		D		S		C		L
	S	H	E	E	T		J	U	D	O
S		S		A		N		F		T		U
M	O	T	O	R		C	A	J	O	L	E	D
I		A		A		E		O		A		E
L	E	S	S	O	N		E	R	A	S	E	S
E		H		H			D		S		T

			Ⓘ					F
O	W	N		L	A	T	E	R
	A	L	P	A	C	A		E
A	X	E		D	R	I	V	E
		T		S	O	L	I	D
	C		H		S	O	Ⓢ	O
G	O	B	I		T	R	A	M
	U		S		I			S
P	R	O	T	O	C	O	L
	S	M	O	G		G	E	L
P	E	A	R	L		R	I	O
	R	Y	E		E	A	T

6.

Tire track **number 6** matches the victim's car.

There are a number of missing letters in the article which spell out **I AM CLOSER THAN YOU THINK**.

PUZZLE 70

```
U N A C C E P T A B L E
N   R   U   U N   C
H O P E S   M   G   L
E   E     T R A D E S M A N
S   G   A       R     I
I   G A R B   P   S A R I
T     I   D I V E S T   N
A N O N   G   B   A U R A
T     O M N I B U S   D
I N N S   E   L   H I R E
N   E A S T E R   R   Q
G O D S   S   S   S E E R  U A
U     A     T   I     A
S T A N D A R D S   T   T
W     I   U   I N A N E
I     I   E   M   N   L
T R I U M P H A N T L Y
```

PUZZLE 71

```
M   A A   S S   O
R E T R O S P E C T I V E
M   G   K V   O   E
M O D E R A T E   R A R E
    N   N N   M   H
L A T T I C E   B Y W A Y
L     E   B   U
A F T E R   T R E A D L E
R   M   P I   S
H E A P   L I G A T U R E
S   L   U   A   U   E
A C C O M M O D A T I N G
O   Y   S   E   E   T
```

PUZZLE 72

7.

Key **number 7** matches the lock on the victim's car.

PUZZLE 73

C	A	H	F	I	B	D	E	G
D	I	F	E	C	G	B	H	A
B	E	G	A	D	H	F	I	C
G	C	A	B	F	E	H	D	I
F	D	B	H	G	I	C	A	E
E	H	I	C	A	D	G	F	B
H	G	C	I	E	F	A	B	D
I	F	D	G	B	A	E	C	H
A	B	E	D	H	C	I	G	F

PUZZLE 74

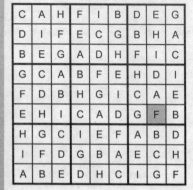

PUZZLE 76

PUZZLE 77

PUZZLE 78

 = 1   = 8   = 5

185 + 185 + 185 = 555

The code to unlock the phone is **555**.

PUZZLE 79

The letters A to Z have been replaced with the numbers 1 to 26.

Sender: Unknown

SHE WAS A RUDE BITTER OLD WOMAN WHO DESERVED EVERYTHING SHE GOT. I'D DO IT AGAIN IF I COULD.

Received: 04:36

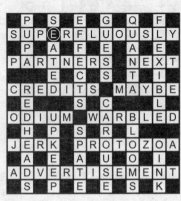

MESSAGE IN THE GRAVEN END
NEWSPAPER PUZZLES:

THE KILLER IS NOT FEMALE

261

PUZZLE 82

L	A	L	L	I	D	M	A	D	R
L	I	C	E	G	M	O	V	E	A
S	P	L	R	A	C	H	I	S	C
J	C	I	A	D	H	A	M	O	R
A	G	R	R	I	S	R	E	S	E
S	H	S	E	E	L	Y	F	Y	M
M	S	S	A	M	L	N	E	H	T
I	E	G	R	O	E	N	M	A	R
N	R	A	G	N	T	M	M	A	O
E	O	N	O	N	U	E	G	R	J

PUZZLE 83

S	H	R	E	D	D	E	R		B	L	O	C
O		E		R		N		E		O		O
D	A	N	C	E		O	V	E	R	A	L	L
A		O		S		U		D		D		O
V	A	R	N	I	S	H		U	N		N	S
E			C		G		O	P	T	I	M	A	L
E	N	L	I	S	T	S		C		U		F
R		A		P		A		E		
A	D	M	I	R	E	R		S	I	S	A	L
T		P		E		E		L		L		O
E	A	S	Y		A	Y	R	S	H	I	R	E

PUZZLE 84

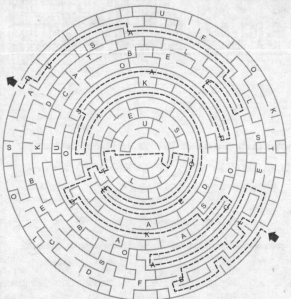

By following the correct path through the maze, you reveal the following message: **BLACKSTONE IS A FRAUD**

This clue was found underneath the *phone*. If you tap out the numbers on an old-fashioned phone with letters on the buttons exactly as they are shown on the note, it reveals the following message:
YOU NEED TO LOOK IN THE SAFE.

G	D	B	H	F	E	C	I	A
I	E	A	C	B	G	F	D	H
F	H	C	A	D	I	E	B	G
H	I	G	B	E	A	D	C	F
C	B	G	D	G	F	A	H	I
A	F	D	I	H	C	G	E	B
E	A	I	G	C	H	B	F	D
D	C	G	F	A	B	I	G	E
B	G	F	E	I	D	H	A	C

By studying the cards on the right, you will see that there are four cards missing: the 2 of clubs, the 4 of diamonds, the 7 of spades, and the 10 of hearts. If you sort these four cards into the order shown on the front of the safe, the code is **41072**.

263

PUZZLE 89

```
V I T R E O U S     A M I R
I   A   N   N       E     H
C O R D(S)  V U L G A T E
E   M   E   E       G   O
    A   M   I N F O R M S
D E C I B E L   I   E   T
I       L       G       A
S   S   E   I N H I B I T
T R A N S I T   T   A
U   D       A   C  (N)  R
R A D I C A L   L E A S E
B   E       I   U       A
S I N K   S C A B B A R D
```

PUZZLE 90

```
E E     A   B       W   A
M A L A Y S I A   B R A N
B   E     S   G   E   O
A   V   E   P I N T     D
T   A   S K I     C O Y
T U T O R S   P O S H   N
L   O   E   E   E   E
E A R T H S   R U E D
D   U       L       E

  E B B S   T I L I N G
N   S   U H   N   O
I   C L U B   A N O I N T
B O A   T O N     T   I
B   P I E R   K   I   S
L   I     A   I   A   T
E L S E   C O N F E T T I
D   T   T   G   E   C
```

PUZZLE 91

This thumbprint does not appear in the "Prints on File" list but has been seen already: **it is listed under Dr. Alan Easton's photo** on the "Meet the Team" profile pages (4–5).

PUZZLE 92

```
S L A   I   A   O   J
Q U I Z Z I C A L   G O O
U   G   I   E   E   R   C
A L A R M   B E R S E R K
T   T   U   O   T       E
  S U B(T)E X T   I F F Y
J   R   H       R   R   S
E Y E S   A S S U M E D
R       V   P   M   S   J
S C A L E N E   O C H R E
E   Q   N   E   U   M  (W)
Y O U   U N D E R T A K E
S   A   E   Y   S   N   L
```

264

Q	U	A	N	P	A	R	T	N	E
P	S	L	H	T	O	R	B	C	R
S	E	C	E	G	R	A	T	O	U
E	E	N	R	D	N	N	N	U	S
T	R	I	S	B	A	D	M	A	I
Y	C	E	U	H	E	T	O	W	N
L	E	C	L	E	G	H	E	A	I
I	U	N	E	H	A	W	R	L	N
M	S	T	R	I	T	I	F	E	D
A	F	N	A	D	N	E	C	S	E

50	51	52	58	60	61	62	63	64	65
49	53	57	59	79	80	94	95	67	66
48	54	56	78	81	93	99	97	96	68
40	47	55	77	82	92	100	98	89	69
39	41	46	76	83	85	91	90	88	70
35	38	42	45	75	84	86	87	71	25
34	36	37	43	44	74	73	72	26	24
14	33	32	31	30	29	28	27	22	23
13	15	16	17	18	19	20	21	1	3
12	11	10	9	8	7	6	5	4	2

The puzzle is directing the police to dig up the paving stone **number 83**.

The safe in the floor can be opened using the code **9876**.

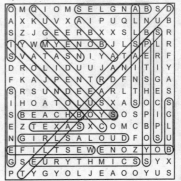

PUZZLE 98

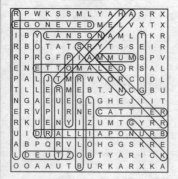

POL ROGERS is in the list of words to find, but it is not in the word search.

PUZZLE 99

PUZZLE 100

PUZZLE 101

The letters A to Z have been replaced with the numbers 1 to 26.

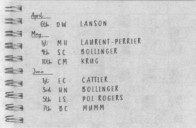

April
6th   DW   LANSON

May
1st   MH   LAURENT-PERRIER
9th   SC   BOLLINGER
10th CM   KRUG

June
1st   EC   CATTIER
3rd   HN   BOLLINGER
5th   LS   POL ROGERS
7th   BC   MUMM

The initials all represent the names of people listed in Wonderment's ledger and which bottle of champagne they bought from the victim.

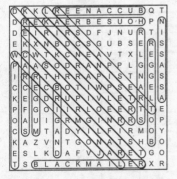

FORGER is in the list of words to find, but it is not in the word search.

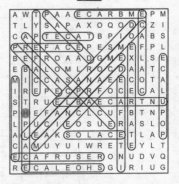

J	U	M	P	I	E	S	T		M	E	S	H
A		O		N		I		D	X		O	
Z	E	B	R	A		L		I	M	P	E	L
Z		S		D		V		S	O		L	
	R	E	M	E	M	B	E	R	E	D		
T		R		Q		R		E		T	A	
W	O	E	F	U	L		S	L	E	E	P	Y
I			T		A		E		I	D	S	
S	T	R	U	C	T	U	R	E	D			
T		E		I		R		V		I	T	
T	I	M	A	G	E		E		I	N	F	E	R
N		T		S		K		N		F	U	
G	U	S	T			G	A	R	G	O	Y	L	E

The control sample has 4 black, 6 grey and 7 white elements. None of the chemical samples of champagne match the control sample. **All the champagnes are fake.**

PUZZLE 106

D	C	H	A	F	G	I	E	B
E	G	B	H	I	D	F	A	C
F	A	I	C	B	E	D	H	G
G	H	D	B	E	A	C	I	F
A	E	C	I	D	F	B	G	H
I	B	F	G	C	H	E	D	A
H	I	E	F	G	B	A	C	D
C	F	A	D	H	I	G	B	E
B	D	G	E	A	C	H	F	I

PUZZLE 107

P	A	C	E	S		A	F	R	I	C	A	N
O		O		T		C		N		U		
S		U		Y		C		C	H	A	R	M
T	H	R	I	L	L	E	R		A		A	
U		A		I		D		S	L	Y	L	Y
R	E	G	I	S	T	E	R		E		A	
I		E		H			A		L		C	
N			L		S	A	N	D	W	I	C	H
G	L	U	O	N		B		U		B		T
	I		C		T	R	O	L	L	E	Y	S
I	N	L	A	Y		O		A		R		M
	E		L		A		T		A		A	
A	N	N	E	L	I	D		E	L	L	E	N

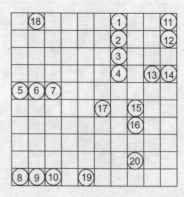

PUZZLE 108

This is one possible
solution to the puzzle

268

They looked through the hole in the ceiling
to tell when it was night, then left through
the glass tunnel, which wasn't then hot.

CRIME 5: DR. ANTHONY MASTERSON

PUZZLE 113

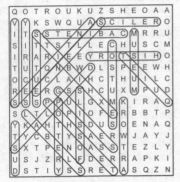

CURATOR is in the list of words to find, but it is not in the word search.

PUZZLE 114

T	A	K	E	S			T	W	I	N	I	N	G
U		N		U		U		U		U		E	
M		O		P	S		A	Z	U	R	E		
E	S	C	A	P	I	S	T		Z		V		
S		K		O	L		F	L	O	E	S		
C	H	E	R	R	I	E	S		E			Q	
E		D		T			S		J			U	
T	H	I	N	G		O		A	J			W	
	A		D		J	O	Y	S	T	I	C	K	
P	I	X	I	E		S		O		T		I	
	R		G		E		N		S		N		
B	Y	G	O	N	E	S		S	W	U	N	G	

PUZZLE 115

C	A	F	E		A	B	N	O	R	M	A	L
R		O		N		U		U		A		I
A	G	I	L	E	L	Y		T	E	N	E	T
F		S		V		I		S		M		T
T	I	T	R	E		N	E	T	B	A	L	L
S			R		G		R		D			E
M	I	G	H	T	Y		R	E	D	E	E	M
A		R		H		P		T				E
N	E	A	T	E	N	S		C	I	D	E	R
S		D		L		Y		H		O		M
H	O	U	S	E		C	A	E	S	U	R	A
I		A		S		H		D		S		I
P	O	L	I	S	H	E	D		W	E	E	D

PUZZLE 116

2	6	5	9	1	7	3	4	8
8	4	7	6	5	3	9	1	2
9	1	3	4	8	2	5	6	7
5	9	4	2	3	1	7	8	6
7	2	6	8	4	5	1	3	9
3	8	1	7	6	9	4	2	5
4	5	9	1	2	6	8	7	3
1	7	2	3	9	8	6	5	4
6	3	8	5	7	4	2	9	1

The highlighted squares are 6 and 4.

PUZZLE 117

3	9	7	2	4	6	5	1	8
8	1	4	3	5	9	6	2	7
6	2	5	1	7	8	4	3	9
2	7	6	8	3	5	1	9	4
4	8	3	9	1	2	7	6	5
9	5	1	7	6	4	2	8	3
1	3	9	4	2	7	8	5	6
5	4	2	6	8	3	9	7	1
7	6	8	5	9	1	3	4	2

The highlighted squares are **1** and **3**.

PUZZLE 118

2	7	3	6	9	1	8	4	5
8	1	4	7	5	2	3	6	9
9	6	5	3	4	8	2	7	1
4	3	6	9	1	7	5	8	2
7	8	1	5	2	3	4	9	6
5	9	2	8	6	4	7	1	3
6	4	8	1	3	5	9	2	7
3	2	9	4	7	6	1	5	8
1	5	7	2	8	9	6	3	4

The highlighted squares are **9** and **5**.

The full code to get in the door is **641395**.

PUZZLE 119

The letterboard is missing letters, which spell out
U DARE TO CALL ME A LIAR AGAIN.

PUZZLE 120

PUZZLE 121

```
L E A P F R O G   M U C K
  L     O     A     E   I   O
G A L L I C   C A S I N G
  S     E     E   K   D     T
S T O M P   T O P I A R Y
  I     I   B     R     A
A N E C D O T E   E E L S
  R     L     U   X   C   T
C O M M U N I C A T I O N
  B     A   C     E     C   O
A J A R   E M P L O Y E D
  E     G     T   C     R
E C U A D O R   S T E R N
  T     R   L   E     A   A
T I D I E D   P I G S T Y
  N     N   E     I   O   U
O G R E   N I C K N A M E
```

PUZZLE 122

Each employee will change the status of all lockers that have a number that is a multiple of that employee's number. Conversely, every locker will have its status changed by the employees that are numbered by one of the locker's factors.

Locker 1, which has one factor, will be open at the end, as the only employee who touches it is employee 1, who opens it. Locker 2, with two factors, will be closed, since the only two employees to touch it are employee 1, who opens it, and then employee 2, who closes it.

Locker 3, also with two factors, will also be closed at the end. On the other hand, Locker 4, which has three factors (1, 2, and 4), will be open, shut, and open again.

As the lockers are closed to begin with, any time a locker number has an even number of factors, it will end up closed. Numbers with an odd number of factors will end up open. All perfect squares have an odd number, which is why the lockers with these numbers end up open.

The lockers left open are 1, 4, and 9 and, therefore the code to the combination lock is **149**.

PUZZLE 123

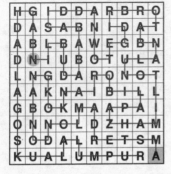

PUZZLE 124

B	I	H	F	G	C	A	E	D
C	G	E	A	D	H	I	B	F
D	A	F	B	E	I	G	H	C
F	E	I	D	C	B	H	A	G
G	C	D	E	H	A	B	F	I
H	B	A	G	I	F	D	C	E
I	F	G	H	B	E	C	D	A
A	H	C	I	F	D	E	G	B
E	D	B	C	A	G	F	I	H

273

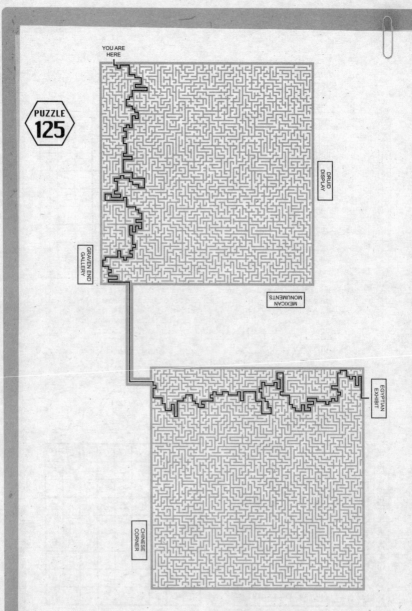

YOU ARE HERE

PUZZLE 125

DRUID DISPLAY

GRAVEN END GALLERY

MEXICAN MONUMENTS

EGYPTIAN EXHIBIT

CHINESE CORNER

The next clue is in the **Egyptian Area** of the museum.

PUZZLE 126

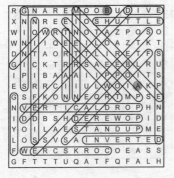

PUZZLE 127

G	A	D	F	B	H	I	E	C
H	C	B	I	A	E	F	D	G
I	F	E	D	G	C	H	A	B
D	B	A	E	F	I	C	G	H
F	E	H	G	C	B	D	I	A
C	G	I	H	D	A	E	B	F
E	D	F	B	H	G	A	C	I
B	H	C	A	I	D	G	F	E
A	I	G	C	E	F	B	H	D

PUZZLE 128

23	22	21	20	19	18	17	11	10	9
24	26	27	54	55	56	16	14	12	8
25	28	53	60	59	58	57	15	13	7
29	52	61	63	64	65	66	1	6	5
30	51	62	95	94	74	73	67	2	4
31	50	96	99	100	93	75	72	68	3
32	42	49	97	98	92	89	76	71	69
33	41	43	48	91	90	88	85	77	70
34	37	40	44	47	87	86	84	81	78
35	36	38	39	45	46	83	82	80	79

The next clue can be found in **square 78**.

PUZZLE 129

1 = Mummy A
2 = Mummy D
3 = Mummy E
4 = Mummy B
5 = Mummy C
6 = Mummy F

PUZZLE 130

PUZZLE 131

PUZZLE 132

Take the first letter from each of the 5-letter groups to spell out the following sentence:
YOU RUINED MY LIFE SO NOW ITS TIME FOR YOU TO PAY.

PUZZLE 133

The Egyptian **gold display** would be covering the X.

PUZZLE 134

The hieroglyphs scratched into the side of the display cabinet spell out **FIND TAPE**.

PUZZLE 135

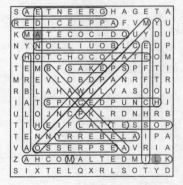

PUZZLE 136

PUZZLE
137

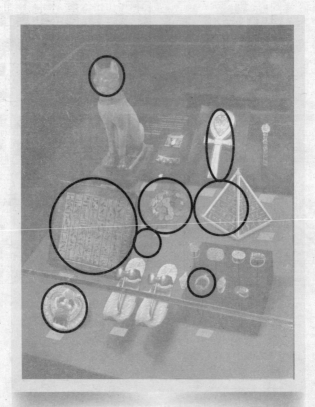

PUZZLE 138

```
W H I S P E R S   A J A R
E   N   R   E   S   E   E
A N K L E   V   C R O W N
K   S   R   I   H   P   D
    R E D E C O R A T E
D   C   Q   W   O   R   R
E X O D U S   S L U D G E
F   C   I   T   M   Y   D
E G O I S T I C A L
N   N   I   P   S   S   C
D O U B T   T   T O P A Z
E   T   E   O   E   O   A
R O S Y   O P E R A T O R
```

PUZZLE 139

```
S W E D E N   A M A N D A
 E   E E   E W N   I
J A V A   W R A N G L E S
 T   D S   K   L
W(H)I S K   D E C E I V E
 E   E T   N     I
T R E A S U R E T R O V E
 E   N   D O   A
A D J U D G E   P O U C H
 N   S G   S   I
C L O I S T(E)R   T O O K
 O   T E   I E   U
B A R Y O N   P H R A S E
```

PUZZLE 140

```
E I H F B A G C D
F C G I D H B A E
B A D G C E F I H
D G I E A F C H B
C F B D H G A E I
A H E B I C D G F
G B F A E I H D C
H E A C F D I B G
I D C H G B E G I
```

PUZZLE 141

```
E N L A R G E D   A   C
S A   R     R U R A L
C A R T O O N S   T   N
A G   U I   H O N K
P R O M I N E N C E   E
I     A D C   N I L
S     N A S C E N T   L
M E N U   H     I C O N
M   F A N A T I C   N
V I S A   I   A V I D
G   C H A N N E L     U
R O T   D A L       U
A   U N D E R L Y I N G
S T I R   E     R   H
I   E   R E A R M O S T
H O A R D     T   N   E
N   S   C L E A N S E R
```

PUZZLE 142

Genuine coins could have had a date but **NOT** BCE inscribed on them.

PUZZLE 143

(5) (2) (1) (6) (3) (4)

PUZZLE 144

PUZZLE 145

```
MESSAGE IN THE GRAVEN END
    NEWSPAPER PUZZLES:

KEEP LOOKING BACK AT ALL THE CLUES
```

PUZZLE 146

Yes, the printout does match the DNA sequence the victim was looking at - it's upside down.

PUZZLE 147

```
S D   [T] S S
A P P E A S E R   O A T S
  R   S   P   U   U     I
L U S T   I G N O R A N T
  C   R   R   K       G
R E F U G E S   W O R S E
      C   S   N       P
S E C T S   R E V E R S E
  X   C   E   R     [H]
M U R M U R E D   A V O N
  D   U   U   F   B   O
L[E]S S   E Q U A L I T Y
  D   H   T   L   E   S
```

PUZZLE 148

```
A G A R   D E L I R I U M
P   C   M   R   N   N   I
P R O X I E S   H U S[K]S
R   R   S   A   O   I   M
O W N   J   T   S E P I A
X       U N Z I P   I   N
I   O   D       I   D   A
M   D   G R A F T       G
A D D L E   F   A   P I E
T   B   M   F   B   I   M
E V A D E   O B L I Q U E
L   L   N   R   E   U   N
Y U L E T I D E   G E N T
```

PUZZLE 149

```
R U G S   A B A C U S E S
E   U   S   O   H   W   E
Q U I P P E D   A R O S E
U   L   O   K   R   L   P
I N T E R M[I]N A B L Y
T   A       N   C   E   B
A W A R D S   S T A N Z A
L   X   I   E   E     [L]
  C O N C E N T R A T E D
S  [L] A   J   I   U   N
K N O L L   O B S E R V E
U   T   L   I   E   F   S
A L L A Y I N G   A S K S
```

PUZZLE 150

```
C E G U A R R O V I
T R E F A D P E T S
R T A I S E M S R I
O P T N T N A T E O
U P Y D E R I T V N
S Y B N U W R E O I
I T O E D N A R C N
R U N E Y T R R E V
E C D D B A W A S T
S G N I K C T N E M
```

PUZZLE 151

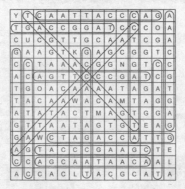

The unused letters in the puzzle (that aren't C, T, A OR G) spell out **YOU KNOW ME WELL**.

PUZZLE 152

The missing number is **45**. In each column, each number is 3 times the one above.

PUZZLE 153

PUZZLE 154

G	C	F	D	A	I	H	E	B
H	A	B	C	F	E	I	D	G
E	I	D	B	G	H	A	F	C
A	E	I	F	D	B	C	G	H
F	D	C	H	I	G	B	A	E
B	G	H	A	E	C	D	I	F
C	F	G	I	H	D	E	B	A
D	H	E	G	B	A	F	C	I
I	B	A	E	C	F	G	H	D

282

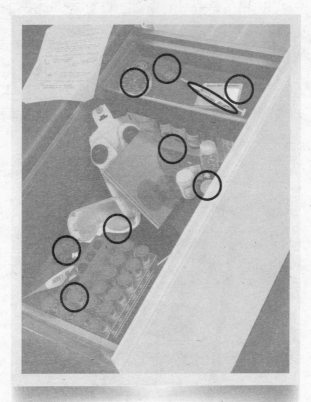

PUZZLE 156

PUZZLE 157

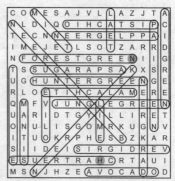

PUZZLE 158

PUZZLE 159

Josie should take half of each tablet today, then the other halves tomorrow.

PUZZLE 160

The symptoms Dr. Easton described match **potassium cyanide** poisoning.

PUZZLE 161

PUZZLE 162

PUZZLE 163

The letters of the keyboard have been rearranged to spell **SHE GOT TOO CLOSE**.

PUZZLE 164

Delete one letter from the pair to make the following message: **HAVE YOU TRIED LOOKING UNDER THE DESK.**

The path through the maze reveals the password for the USB drive: **2019.**